ECLIPSE

The Sun

$\longrightarrow$

for scaled distance
to the Earth and
Moon see page 175

Also by J. P. McEvoy

Introducing Stephen Hawking
Introducing Quantum Theory

ECLIPSE

The Science and History
of
Nature's Most Spectacular Phenomenon

J. P. McEVOY

FOURTH ESTATE • *London*

For Emily, Muirenn, Joel
and the baby arriving with the eclipse
in August 1999

First published in Great Britain in 1999 by
Fourth Estate Limited
6 Salem Road
London W2 4BU

1 3 5 7 9 10 8 6 4 2

A catalogue record for this book is available from the British Library

ISBN 1-84115-184-X

Designed by Robert Updegraff
Illustrations by Mark McEvoy
Printed in Great Britain by T. J. International, Padstow, Cornwall

CONTENTS

PROLOGUE

Darkness at Noon: Baja Mexico, 11 July 1991

Stretching over 1,300 km south of the California state line between San Diego and Tijuana is a peninsula of mountains, deserts and plains ending at one of the most beautiful beaches in the world. Fine golden sand for miles and miles slopes into the azure Sea of Cortés and the Pacific Ocean. The peninsula, called Baja California, is actually part of Mexico. In the heat of the summer of 1991 I arrived, planning to view my first total eclipse of the Sun.

The morning of 11 August is bright and clear. Amid the palm trees and cactus plants all along the beach, tripods are being set up in the sand, an army of straw hats and Bermuda shorts appear as far as the eye can see. Everyone is buoyant. Not a single cloud in the sky, though still a few hours to go. Totality would be unusually long today at Los Cabos, 6 minutes 26 seconds, close to the theoretical maximum for a solar eclipse. The Moon's shadow, when it reaches Baja, will be 260 km wide, moving along the beach at a speed of about 40 km per minute. As the bell in the small church tolls 10:00 a.m., the crowd makes final adjustments to telescopes and cameras. The long wait is over. Twenty-three minutes to go.

First contact occurs at 10:23:17 as the Moon's disk just touches the Sun's. The sky continues to be cloudless and no one is thinking of the weather. The show has begun.

In earlier times humanity held its breath during this solar disappearing act, offering sacrifices to appease the evil spirits who might destroy humanity's source of heat and life itself. Slowly the Moon cuts deeper and deeper into the Sun's image and it is now obvious that the two disks have the same diameter, a remarkable coincidence. The light fades imperceptibly.

Two small Japanese girls watch the progress of the eclipse through special Mylar sunglasses, while their mother watches anxiously. The Moon's shadow is now sweeping across the globe towards us on the beach at Los Cabos at twice the speed of Concorde. In an orbit above the earth, a weather satellite photographs the shadow of the Moon every half-hour during its journey.

As second contact approaches, the Sun has been reduced to a thin crescent and now breaks up into a string of bright beads. These are known as Baily's beads, caused by the streaming of the last rays of sunlight between mountains at the edge of the

Baily's beads

Moon. One by one the beads disappear until only one is left, radiating brightly from a single point on the edge of the eclipse, like a diamond ring.

My watch reads 11:47:40 and the miracle happens: second contact. The diamond ring disappears and a delicate pearly white halo springs into view around the eclipsed Sun. This is the corona. I have 6 minutes and 26 seconds. I look at the sky map and locate four planets in the noonday sky, lined up just to the east of the eclipsed Sun. Mercury and Jupiter are the closest, then Mars and Venus. The twin stars Castor and Pollux are clear and bright in the darkened sky, quite near the Sun. Sirius is just due south of the Sun. Through my telescope I see massive pink gaseous formations floating in the Sun's atmosphere, the solar prominences.

The diamond ring

I look away at my fellow sky-gazers along the beach. It is like a scene from Spielberg's *Close Encounters of the Third Kind*. Hundreds stand transfixed, motionless, staring directly up into the sky. No goggles or Mylar glasses are needed now. There is not a sound — even birds have stopped chirping. In the distance, I see what appears to be a sunset in all directions, 360° around the horizon. This is the illuminated Earth outside the canopy of darkness under the Moon's shadow.

I check my stopwatch as third contact approaches. Then at 11:54:06, the corona disappears. In its place, the diamond ring effect and Baily's beads repeat in reverse order. Cheers of excitement ripple through the crowd. A sliver of sunlight is now visible, and safety viewing devices are taken up to guard against the invisible ultraviolet waves. The Darkness at Noon is over.

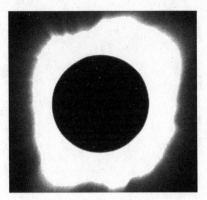

The corona

One hour, fourteen minutes and forty seconds later, fourth contact occurs at 13:18:46. The Moon moves away from the Sun and the full disk returns. Everyone seems satisfied. The eclipse-chasers of the world have had their day in the Moon's shadow. The travel, the hassles, the expense have all been worth it, viewing one of the greatest eclipses of the twentieth century.

UNDERSTANDING AN ECLIPSE

A solar eclipse . . . is a gift to us from the Creator.
Johannes Kepler, 1605

T HE SYSTEMATIC UNDERSTANDING of the motion of heavenly bodies was one of the earliest problems confronting humankind. The development of conceptual models to reproduce this motion is one of the great stories of the history of science.

Even the most casual observer knows that the Sun and the Moon are continuously changing position in the sky. And surely all would agree that the Sun's motion appears to be regular. But other observations are more puzzling. Many people are surprised to see the Moon high in the daytime sky. Why are bright wandering 'stars', the planets, often seen close to the Moon or the setting Sun? Why does the pole star, signposted by the stars of the Plough, never change position? What is the significance of the constellations along the Sun's path?

How can one make sense of all this? The best way is to use a model of the sky called the celestial sphere, an imaginary surface upon which may be represented the motions of the Sun, Moon, stars and planets as seen from the Earth.

Apparent Motion of the Sun and the Moon: The Celestial Sphere

Suppose a sphere that contains the whole universe is drawn with the Earth as its centre, as shown in Figure I.I. The outer shell is an imaginary infinitely large dome onto which the positions of the stars and all other celestial bodies are projected. At any one time, we can see only half of this sphere from our position on the Earth. The celestial sphere works as a model because we are interested only in the directions of celestial bodies, not their distances from the Earth. The celestial equator is a projection of the Earth's equator onto the sphere. Directly above the Earth's north geographical pole is the north pole star, Polaris, marking the position of the north celestial pole. This star appears stationary in the sky as the other stars appear to revolve around it because the axis of the Earth's rotation passes through it. (It is actually nearly a degree from the north celestial pole itself, but this is close enough for it to appear more or less fixed.) Instead of the Earth's rotating in one direction, the sphere is imagined to turn in the opposite direction once every 24 hours so that all the stars complete one cycle every day. This simulates what we see from the apparently stationary Earth.

The Sun moves around the celestial sphere on a path called the ecliptic, describing a complete 360° circuit at a rate of approximately 1° per day in its annual cycle of 365 days. The Moon's path on the celestial sphere differs distinctly from the Sun's. First, the Moon moves more swiftly than the Sun, completing a circuit

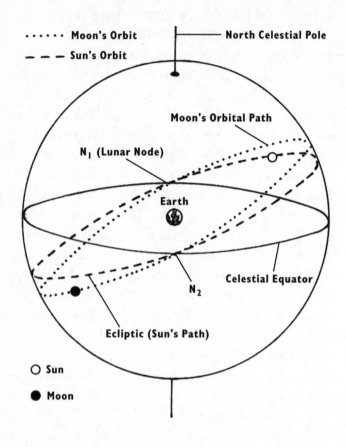

Figure 1.1. The celestial sphere, showing the paths of the Sun and Moon and the position of the lunar nodes.

of the celestial sphere in 29.5 days as seen from the Earth. Second, the Moon's orbit has a different orientation from the Sun's, intersecting the ecliptic at an angle of about 5°, as shown in Figure 1.1. The intersections of the paths of the Sun and the Moon defines two points on the ecliptic called the nodes of the Moon's orbit. The nodes, denoted by the letter N in Figure 1.1, are crucial to the study of eclipses. The arrows showing the direction of the orbital motion of the Moon indicate that one node, N_1, is the descending node, where the Moon crosses the celestial equator from north to south. The other node, N_2, is the ascending node, where the Moon crosses the celestial equator from south to north.

To study eclipses, it is necessary to consider the motion of the Sun and the Moon simultaneously. The Sun advances about 1° per day along the ecliptic, and the Moon moves in the same direction at about 12° per day along its orbital path. As the Moon completes a circuit of the celestial sphere about twelve times faster than the Sun, the Moon is always catching the Sun up and passing it.

With the celestial sphere defined and understood, all aspects of the apparent motion of the Sun and Moon necessary to describe eclipses are in place. However, it should be kept in mind that though this model may be useful, it is of course not a true picture of nature. The Sun does not move around the Earth. In fact, the opposite is true. Nevertheless, the celestial sphere model shows the sky as it appears to an observer on the Earth. So it is possible to speak of the 'Sun orbiting the Earth'

17

in terms of the celestial sphere. The model allows us to define the positions of celestial bodies, and greatly simplifies the visualisation of their motion. It is used by astronomers the world over to measure and report observations of Sun and Moon, planets and stars. During the eighteenth century celestial globes based on the celestial-sphere model were popular accessories among the upper classes. Definitely *de rigueur* in fashionable British and European salons.

A solar eclipse happens when the Moon moves into alignment between the Sun and the Earth, casting its shadow on the Earth and blocking off the Sun's light. Alternatively, if the Moon moves into alignment with the Sun but behind the Earth, the Earth's shadow falls on the Moon. This is called a lunar eclipse. If the orbits of the Sun and the Moon were in the same plane, a solar eclipse would occur at every new Moon and a lunar eclipse would occur at every full Moon. This doesn't happen because the orbit of the Moon is inclined at 5° to the orbit of the Earth around the Sun, as shown in Figure 1.1. The conditions for an eclipse to occur are that the Moon must be new or full and close to one of the nodes. If the new Moon is close to a node, a solar eclipse may occur; if the full Moon is close to a node, a lunar eclipse may occur. As we shall see, the proximity of the Moon to a node is critical. But first, we shall look more closely at the changing phase of the Moon as it moves in its orbit, and the relation of this to eclipses.

Figure 1.2. 'The First Lecture in Geography and Astronomy', 1748, based on the celestial-sphere model of the sky.

The Moon and the Earth: Phases

One aspect of the Moon's motion which is important for understanding eclipses is the cycle of the phases it presents to the Earth during the course of a month. This is illustrated in Figure 1.3. New Moon marks the start of the cycle, when the Moon cannot be seen because it is in the same direction as the Sun and the illuminated, sunlit side faces away from the Earth. A day later, however, the Moon has moved away from the Sun and is seen as a slim crescent in the evening sky just after sunset before disappearing over the horizon. A few days later, the waxing, growing Moon is seen higher in the sky, now increasing its angular distance from the Sun at a rate of just over 12° per day. (It moves through one complete cycle of 360° in a little over 29.5 days, a period called a synodic month.) Between the 7th and 8th days the Moon reaches first quarter, making a right angle with the Sun as seen from the Earth, and the right half of the Moon is now illuminated. Between the 8th and 15th days the illuminated portion continues to grow until midway through the cycle, when full Moon is reached.

At full Moon the entire lunar disk is illuminated and 180° separate the Moon from the Sun. It is in this position that a lunar eclipse is possible, depending on how close the full Moon is to one of its nodes. As the month plays out, the illuminated portion decreases. The waning Moon reaches third quarter after about 22 days, when only the left half is illuminated. The Moon again makes a right angle with the Sun as seen from the

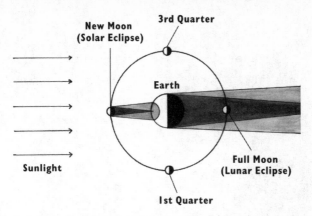

Figure 1.3. The four chief phases of the Moon and the times when eclipses can occur.

Earth. The Moon will rise before the Sun, visible in the morning sky. After last quarter the Moon moves closer and closer to the Sun, showing a progressively thinner crescent. On the 27th and 28th days the Moon is seen only just before sunrise, a sliver in the morning sky as new Moon approaches. After 29.5 days the Moon passes out of view again at new Moon. If the new Moon is close enough to one of its nodes a solar eclipse will occur. After new Moon, the cycle starts all over again. Figure 1.3 shows that a lunar eclipse can occur only at full Moon, and a solar eclipse can occur only at new Moon.

A PENNY IN YOUR EYE: A DIY ECLIPSE

It is easy to simulate a solar eclipse. First, take a circular drinks coaster about 10 cm in diameter in your left hand, and extend it to arm's length. Then take a penny in your right hand. Close

Figure 1.4. Making your own solar eclipse.

one eye. Now view the two disks along the same axis, and adjust the position of the penny closer and closer to your eye until it just obscures your view of the coaster. You have just simulated a total eclipse of the Sun. For the 2 cm penny and a 10 cm coaster, and assuming arm's length to be 70 cm, the penny will be about 14 cm from your eye.

The simplicity of this simulated solar eclipse may suggest that a real solar eclipse is a common phenomenon. But size considerations make a solar eclipse a remarkable event. The Sun is about four hundred times larger than the Moon. But it is also about four hundred times as distant as the Moon. As a result, the Sun and Moon appear to an observer on the surface of the Earth to be almost the same size in the sky. When the Moon is new and precisely aligned with the Sun and the Earth, the two disks can overlap nearly exactly, and a solar eclipse occurs. The Moon obstructs the Sun's light and casts its shadow on the Earth.

To demonstrate how unusual the phenomenon of a solar eclipse is, a scale drawing has been made of the Sun, Moon and Earth and the distances between them. The common scale has been achieved by using the Moon's diameter as a measuring unit, a *Moon*. The scaled sizes and distances are listed in Table 1A. Note that on this scale the Earth's diameter is 3.66 *Moons*, the Sun's diameter is 400 *Moons*, the Earth–Moon distance is 109 *Moons* and the Earth–Sun distance is 42,816 *Moons*. If we choose a scale of 1 *Moon* = 0.5 mm, the Moon would look like this: · ; the Earth would be 1.83 mm, as indicated in Table 1A, and look like this: ● . The Sun would be 200 mm in diameter.

Table 1A. Dimensions for a scale drawing of a solar eclipse.

Measurement	Metric	Units	Millimetres	Pages
	(thousands of km)	(1 unit = 0.5 mm)	(1 page =123 mm)	
Moon diameter	3.48	1.00	0.50	—
Earth diameter	12.74	3.66	1.83	—
Sun diameter	1,394.00	400.57	200.29	1.63
Distance E–M	380.00	109.20	54.60	0.44
Distance E–S	149,000.00	42,816.00	21,408.00	174.05

Part of the Sun is drawn to scale on the inside front cover of this book. The separation between the two bodies would be 54.6

mm, as shown on page 175, where the Earth and the Moon and their separation are shown to scale. The Earth's diameter is 1.83 mm to scale, and the Moon's diameter is 0.5 mm. Why page 175? Because we need nearly the entire extent of this book, from the inside front cover to page 175, to represent on this scale the distance from the Sun to the Earth. This is with all the pages opened out like an accordion, double-sided. At this distance the image of the Sun viewed from the Earth shrinks to 0.5 mm, and is just small enough to be obstructed by the image of the Moon, which is also 0.5 mm across on this scale.

TYPES OF SOLAR ECLIPSE

Not all solar eclipses are alike. There are three different types, defined in terms of the shadow produced by the Moon. Like a sundial or even a large straw hat, the Moon casts a shadow in sunlight, and in the Moon's case the shadow is long enough to reach the Earth, causing an eclipse. Most of the time the cone-shaped lunar shadow is projected out into space, past the Earth. However, when the conditions of the Moon's phase and orbital position are right, near a node at new Moon, the shadow strikes the Earth. As shown in Figure 1.5, one of three types of solar eclipse will occur, depending on the exact circumstances of the Earth–Moon–Sun alignment and on the Earth–Moon distance.

There are two parts to any shadow produced by an extended light source like the Sun. The umbra is the zone of total shadow, from within which no part of the Sun can be seen. If

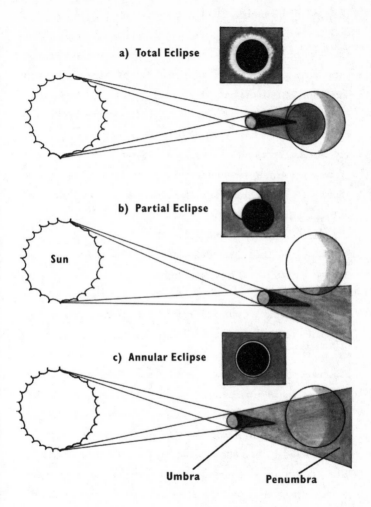

a) **Total Eclipse**

b) **Partial Eclipse**

Sun

c) **Annular Eclipse**

Umbra   Penumbra

Figure 1.5. Types of solar eclipse: total (a), partial (b) and annular (c).

the tip of the umbral shadow cone reaches the Earth, those within the small region where it falls will see a total eclipse. Outside the umbra but within the penumbra, the light is not completely cut off by the Moon, and an observer on the Earth sees some part of the Sun, experiencing a partial eclipse. A total eclipse is the most interesting type. For an observer within the umbra, the faint corona surrounding the Sun can be seen if the sky is clear of cloud. The corona is a very thin gas, mostly hydrogen, forming the outer atmosphere of the Sun, which appears as a halo during a total eclipse – it is in fact the most distinguishing characteristic of a total eclipse. A partial eclipse can also be seen when only the penumbra strikes the Earth. None of the special characteristics of totality such as the corona are seen during a partial eclipse.

In an annular eclipse, the Moon is aligned in front of the Sun but does not completely cover the Sun's disk because the umbra does not quite reach the Earth. It is still a striking visual effect, with sunlight streaming out from a ring around the Moon's outer rim. This gives the eclipse its name: annular means 'ring-like'. As in a partial eclipse, the faint solar corona is not seen in an annular eclipse, for it is overwhelmed by the bright direct sunlight from the annular ring. An annular eclipse can be demonstrated by a slight variation in the DIY demonstration. Align the penny as before, just covering the coaster, then move the penny away from your eye slightly. You will see a ring of the coaster appear around the penny. *Voilà* – an annular eclipse!

The fact that a central alignment can cause either a total eclipse or an annular eclipse implies that the Earth–Moon distance varies. The Moon is not always close enough to the Earth to obscure the entire face of the Sun. In fact, both the Earth–Moon distance and the Earth–Sun distance change continuously as the Earth and Moon trace out their orbits. The values given in Table 1A for these distances are averages: at a given moment their orbital distances can be more or less than these values. Consequently, the Moon is sometimes not close enough to eclipse the Sun totally, even when perfectly aligned, and an annular eclipse happens instead.

The variation of the Earth–Moon and Earth–Sun distances is due to the non-circularity of their orbits. This is a characteristic of all orbiting bodies, and was one of the discoveries made by the German astronomer Johannes Kepler (1571–1630) early in the seventeenth century. Kepler had proposed a set of laws for planetary motion which were completely at odds with contemporary theories. The first law stated that all the planets, including the Earth, move in orbits around the Sun which are elongated circles called ellipses. Furthermore, said Kepler, the Sun is not at the centre of the planet's orbit, but sits at one of two points on each side of the centre, each called a focus.

Kepler's second law proposed another revolutionary idea: that the planets do not move uniformly, but continuously slow down when moving away from the Sun, and speed up when moving towards the Sun. A planet moves fastest at the point in its elliptical

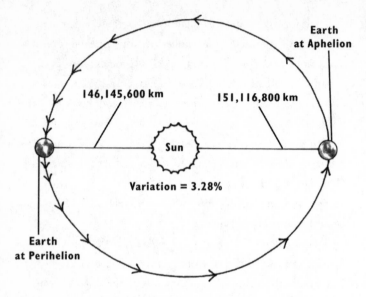

Earth
at Aphelion

146,145,600 km

151,116,800 km

Sun

Variation = 3.28%

Earth
at Perihelion

Figure 1.6. The Earth's orbit, showing the variation of the Earth–Sun distance.

orbit where it makes its closest approach to the Sun, called perihelion. It moves slowest at the other end of the orbit, when farthest from the Sun, at the point called aphelion. These extreme
points of the orbits are indicated by two prefixes, *peri-* meaning
'near', and *ap-* meaning 'away from'; *-helion* is from the Greek word
for the Sun, *helios*. Figure 1.6 shows the elliptical orbit of the
Earth, with the Sun slightly off-centre (the shape of the ellipse is
exaggerated a little for clarity). The arrows on the orbital path
indicate the speeding up of the Earth as it approaches the Sun
and the slowing down as it recedes from the Sun.

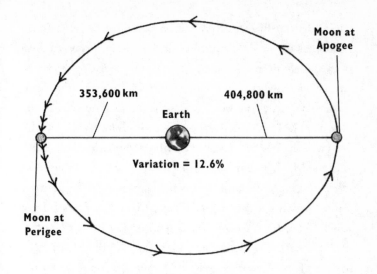

Figure 1.7. The Moon's orbit, showing the variation of the Earth–Moon distance.

The same thing happens with the Moon. In 1687 Isaac Newton (1642–1727) published his theory of gravitation which showed that Kepler's laws were quite general: any body orbiting another attracting body will obey Kepler's laws. So the Moon also moves in an elliptical orbit around the Earth, which lies at one focus of the ellipse. The Moon's orbit around the Earth is shown in Figure 1.7. Again, arrows indicate the speeding up and slowing down of the Moon in its orbit (and again, the ellipse is exaggerated). At the ends of the Moon's orbit there are equivalent points of closest and farthest approach to the Earth, called perigee, 'near the Earth', and apogee, 'away from the Earth'.

In Newton's theory of gravitation the attracting gravitational force between two bodies increases as the distance between them increases. It is this variation of the gravitational pull of the attracting body, the Sun pulling on the Earth and the Earth pulling on the Moon, which causes the speeding up and slowing down of the Earth and the Moon in their orbits.

The distances of closest and farthest approach of the Earth and the Moon are indicated in Figures 1.6 and 1.7. From these distances, the percentage change can be computed. The Earth's orbit is nearly circular, and its distance to the Sun varies only by about 3 per cent. However, the Moon's orbit is more elongated, and the Earth–Moon distance varies by 12 per cent over the course of each monthly cycle. As a result, an observer on the Earth will see the diameter of the Sun change by 2 per cent around its average value, and the angular diameter of the Moon by 8 per cent. Figure 1.8 shows tracings of photographs taken

Figure 1.8. Tracings of photographs of the full Moon at perigee and apogee. The same 100 mm f/10 refracting telescope was used for both photographs (based on Harrington 1997).

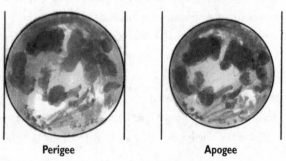

Perigee **Apogee**

Table 1B. Orbital conditions of Earth and Moon for solar eclipses.

Position of Earth	Position of Moon	Type of solar eclipse
Aphelion (maximum distance from Sun) Sun's image maximum	**Perigee** (minimum distance from Earth) Moon's image minimum	Total
Perihelion (minimum distance from Sun) Sun's image maximum	**Apogee** (minimum distance from Earth) Moon's image minimum	Annular

with the same telescope and lens of the full Moon at perigee and apogee. The effect of the orbital variation on the size of the Moon's image as seen from the Earth is clear. Optimum conditions for a solar eclipse are summarised in Table 1B.

THE LINE OF NODES AND THE ECLIPSE SEASON

Figure 1.1 shows the two nodes of the Moon's orbit, the points where the orbit intersects the ecliptic, the path of the Sun on the celestial sphere. The ascending node is defined as the point where the Moon crosses the ecliptic from below to above, south to north. The other node, the descending node, is the point where the Moon crosses the ecliptic from above to below, north to south.

In Figure 1.9 the celestial sphere model has been redrawn with some added features. So that we can further examine the all-important conditions for eclipses, an imaginary line has been drawn connecting the two nodes on the ecliptic. Not surprisingly, this line is known to astronomers as the 'line of nodes'.

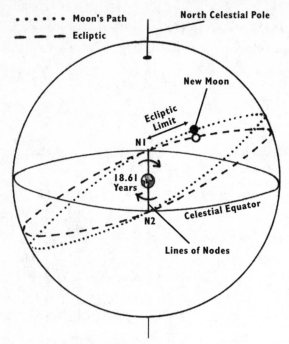

Figure 1.9. The celestial sphere, showing the ecliptic limits and the line of nodes of the Moon's orbit.

The line of nodes rotates slowly in a direction opposite to the Sun's motion, taking 18.61 years to complete one rotation. When this line is aligned with the Sun, an eclipse can take place. As there are two nodes, the alignment occurs about twice a year. The period of time either side of an alignment is called an eclipse season because if a new Moon occurs at this time, it will be near a node and a solar eclipse is likely.

The motion of the line of nodes affects the time between eclipse seasons. The Sun appears to move about 1° per day eastward around the ecliptic, making a circuit of the sky in 365.25 days – a solar year. The line of nodes slowly regresses westward, in the opposite direction, at a rate of 18.61 years for one cycle. So an eclipse year, the time it takes the Sun to travel from alignment with one node to alignment with the same node again, will be less than a solar year. The length of the eclipse year can easily be calculated.

The line of nodes makes one rotation in 18.61 years, so it moves at a rate of $360/(365.25 \times 18.61) = 0.053°$ per day westward around the ecliptic (365.25 being the length of the solar year). The Sun moves at a rate of $360/365.25 = 0.986°$ per day in the opposite direction. To get the combined rate of motion of the line of nodes and the Sun towards each other, add the two together to get 1.039° per day. The length of the eclipse year is therefore 346.62 days (the angular values are given here correct to three decimal places – the precise values do yield 346.62 days). From one node to the next, say the ascending node to the descending node, will take half that time, 173.3 days. These values have important consequences for calculating the frequency at which eclipses take place.

THE ECLIPTIC LIMIT

If the Sun at new Moon is aligned exactly with a node, it is obvious that there will be a solar eclipse. But the new Moon does not have to be exactly at a node for a solar eclipse to occur. Whenever the new Moon is close enough to the node for the two disks just to touch, there will be at least a partial solar eclipse. Look at the position of the Sun and new Moon on the celestial sphere with their disks just touching, in Figure 1.9. This position gives the maximum angular distance the new Moon can be from the node for there to be an eclipse. This distance is known as the ecliptic limit. If the total spread of the ecliptic limit, east plus west, is known as well as the speed of the Sun and Moon, it is possible to calculate the frequency at which eclipses can happen. Figure 1.10 shows a close-up of a part of the ecliptic centred on a node. (The node selected is a descending node, for consistency with examples of eclipses discussed in later chapters.)

The angular spread of the ecliptic limit depends on the tilt of the Moon's orbit, which is a little over 5°. It also depends on the apparent size of the Sun and the Moon which, as we have seen, can vary because the orbital distances of the Earth and the Moon are always changing. Using the appropriate orbital parameters, the maximum angle of the ecliptic limit is found to occur when the Moon is at perigee and the Earth is at perihelion. In this configuration the two disks have their maximum sizes and will 'touch' at a point farthest from the node. This is calculated to be 37.02°, corresponding to a window of about 37.5 days. The minimum is 30.70° for the Moon at apogee and Earth at aphelion. In this case, the two disks have their minimum sizes as seen from the Earth, and will just touch at a point closer to the node. The ecliptic limit can be regarded as a 'dan-

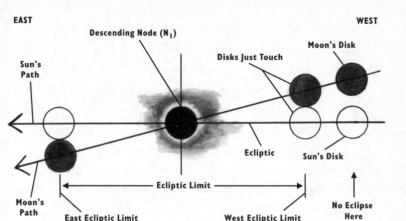

EAST   WEST

Descending Node (N₁)

Moon's Disk

Disks Just Touch

Sun's Path

Ecliptic

Sun's Disk

Ecliptic Limit

Moon's Path

East Ecliptic Limit   **West Ecliptic Limit**

No Eclipse Here

Figure 1.10. The ecliptic limits at a descending node (new Moon in each case).

ger zone' – if a new Moon occurs while the Sun is within this region, there will be a solar eclipse.

Now, in a synodic month of 29.53 days, from one new Moon to the next, the Sun will move a certain fraction of an eclipse year along the ecliptic. This can be calculated as the ratio of the number of days in a synodic month to the number of days in an eclipse year: or 29.53/346.62, which makes 0.085. This fraction of one total revolution of 360° is 30.67°, very close to but less than the minimum angle of the ecliptic limit.

From this result a very interesting conclusion can be drawn. The minimum value of the ecliptic limit, 30.70°, is greater than the angle the Sun moves through during a complete synodic period of the Moon, 30.67°. The Sun will therefore never have enough time to pass through the ecliptic limit without being overtaken by a new Moon, so at least one solar eclipse is inevitable at each node, or two per calendar year. If the orbital conditions are optimum, with the Moon at perigee and the Earth at perihelion, the maximum ecliptic limit of 37.02° applies. The same calculation indicates that two eclipses are possible at each node, for a total of four solar eclipses in a year. The concept of the ecliptic limit thus provides a convenient way of predicting the properties of solar eclipses. It will also prove useful when it comes to explaining the characteristics of the saros series of eclipses.

THE FUTURE OF THE TOTAL SOLAR ECLIPSE

The Renaissance astronomer Johannes Kepler was as impressed as anyone by the coincidence of the 400 : 1 distance/size ratio for the Sun and Moon. In fact, he called the solar eclipse 'a gift to us from the Creator'. He also pointed out in one of his many studies of the heavens that this fortunate situation will not always be true. Millions of years from now, the size of the Moon's orbit will have increased to the point where total solar eclipses won't be possible. All central eclipses will be annular. Here is Kepler's reasoning.

He calculated that when an object's orbital speed increases, the size of its orbit expands. In the case of the Moon, its orbital speed increases as a result of tidal forces. The gravitational force of the Moon pulls on the Earth's oceans and crust, creating the twice-daily tides. Likewise, the Earth's gravity pulls on the Moon, and these tidal effects produce bulges on the Moon's surface. However, the tidal bulges produced on the Earth by the Moon are

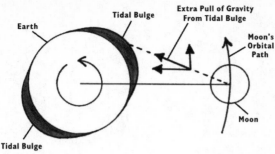

Figure 1.11. The effect of the Earth's tidal bulge on the Moon's orbital speed.

not centred at the point on the Earth's surface directly below the Moon, but are shifted ahead of the Moon because of Earth's faster rate of spin. This is shown in Figure 1.11. So the tidal bulge on the Earth is dragged ahead of the Moon's location in the sky. This bulge exerts an additional gravitational force on the Moon which has a component tending to increase the orbital speed. Over many years, this slight increase in the Moon's orbital speed will cause the Moon to slowly recede from the Earth.

The effect of the Moon inching away from the Earth is barely noticeable on human timescales. But millions of years from now the effects will be real. Our distant descendants will never be able to view a total solar eclipse. At some point in the future the Moon's diameter as seen from the Earth will always appear smaller than the Sun's, and only annular eclipses will be possible. No doubt this has inspired many of the world's obsessive eclipse-chasers who travel all over the world to view the extraordinary phenomenon of a total solar eclipse. They know how lucky we *Homo sapiens* are in the current epoch.

THE
BABYLONIANS,
CHRONICLERS OF
ECLIPSES

How much is one god beyond the other god?

Old Babylonian astronomical text

CLAY FROM BAGHDAD

During the 1870s and early 1880s, numerous clay tablets from Babylonian archaeological sites found their way to antique dealers in Baghdad. The tablets had been found in the ruins of the ancient Assyrian city of Nineveh, where they had once formed part of the royal archive in the most famous library in the ancient Near East. The library was built by King Assurbanipal, who reigned during Assyria's ascendancy in the eighth century BC. This historical treasure was preserved for future scholars when a combined force of Medes and Chaldeans sacked Nineveh in 612 BC destroying the library completely and burying the royal archive in the process.

The Babylonian empire was situated between the two great rivers, the Tigris and the Euphrates, in an area historically known as Mesopotamia – the 'land between two rivers'. Flowing south-eastward, the rivers converge to form a single valley, then proceed in parallel channels for the greater part of their course. Finally, they unite shortly before reaching the Persian Gulf. The joint delta of these rivers forms a plain about 275 km long. As in Egypt with the Nile, the delta offered many advantages to early people, continually attracting settlements for thousands of

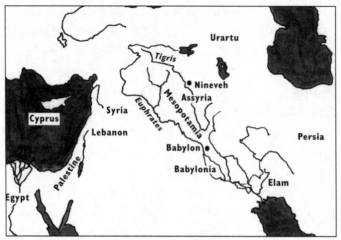

Figure 2.1. The Near East: Mesopotamia, the valley 'between the two rivers'.

years. The fertile valley yielded abundant harvests, workable clay and the nutritious fruit of the date palm. Though large stone deposits were lacking, the early settlers used the local clay for building and even for writing material.

Wars were frequent in ancient Mesopotamia as tribes of hunters from the northern mountains and herdsmen from the south often tried to conquer this rich land. The Sumerians, the earliest inhabitants for whom there are written records, had entered the region by 3700 BC and gradually settled down to a life of farming. The Sumerians are credited with developing the earliest known form of writing.

In the 1880s, the British Museum purchased virtually all the clay tablets from Baghdad via London antique dealers. It was

41

soon realised that among this vast collection were stories of the creation of the world and the great flood, as well as thousands of short texts on mathematics and astronomy. The latter texts contained records of astronomical observations made over hundreds of years in Assyria and Babylonia, and dating back to the third millennium BC. Today over a hundred and thirty thousand of these tablets are still stored at the Museum. It is an astonishing collection that comprises at least 98 per cent of all extant records of Babylonian astronomy.

One set of seventy tablets from Nineveh revealed a vast programme of astronomical observations which had been carried out in the second millennium BC. Known from its opening words as *Enuma Anu Enlil* ('When Heaven and Earth …'), the set is a list, compiled over centuries, of celestial omens believed to have been sent to the king from the gods, warning him of impending disasters. Most of the tablets deal with interpretations of lunar and solar eclipses, conjunctions of planets, and comets, which the Babylonians took as dangerous omens.

OLD BABYLONIAN PERIOD

In the early part of the second millennium BC, Hammurabi, the Semitic king from Arabia, conquered the Sumerians. With this victory he completed the unification of the region 'between the two rivers', and he made Babylon the capital city of his kingdom. Located on the left bank of the Euphrates, some 110 km south of modern Baghdad, for the next four hundred years

Babylon was ruled by the Hammurabi dynasty during what is now called the 'Old Babylonian period', from 2000 to 1600 BC. It was not until after this golden age, however, when the fabled city became the leading centre and capital of the region, that the whole area became known as Babylonia.

The rich heritage of literature, religion and astronomy from the Old Babylonian period found in the ruins of the ancient cities of Babylonia would never have been preserved without a durable medium for recording. The practice of using clay tablets, inherited from the Sumerians, was perfect. These tablets were made from soft clay and written upon with a wedge-shaped stylus, which gave its name to the style of writing, cuneiform: the Latin word *cuneus* means 'wedge'. For permanent records, a completed tablet was dried or baked until hard and usually protected by a clay case or envelope. Practically indestructible when dried, these tablets have provided modern scholars with a wealth of information about this period. Among some of the numerous treasures are thousands of astronomical and mathematical records. For example, the ancient site of Nippur, once the location of an astronomical observatory established by the Assyrian kingdom, has alone yielded some fifty thousand tablets.

Another legacy from Sumeria and the Old Babylonian period was the sexagesimal number system. Thousands of tablets dating from about 1800–1600 BC illustrate a number system that would seem unfamiliar to the modern reader. Instead of the decimal system based on the number 10, the Babylonians used the number 60 as the base (hence the name 'sexagesimal'). Many historians have tried to explain the use of this unusual system of numbers. One theory is that the predominant role of astronomy in Babylonian society was instrumental in the adoption of the sexagesimal system. For example, the solar year is approximately 360 days, a figure which can easily be expressed as 6 x 60. Whatever the origin, the sexagesimal system of numeration has enjoyed a remarkably long life. Remnants survive even today in our units of time, 60 minutes in an hour, and angular measure, 360 degrees in a circle, in spite of the nearly universal acceptance of the decimal system for other counting schemes.

The Old Babylonian period was a time of great advancement for the development of what could be called the 'sciences'. Yet it was one 'science' in particular that characterised the Babylonians' world view — astrology. From early on in this period these people looked to the heavens and attempted to discover some kind of order in the skies. By the beginning of the first millennium BC, the Babylonians had developed skywatching skills and utilised them in the making of a calendar and a system of mathematics, based on the sexagesimal system, to track and simulate the motion of the Sun and Moon.

The regularity of celestial events provided early civilisations with the best means for bringing order and understanding to the cosmos. Their cataloguing of the heavens enabled them to identify celestial cycles of time and thus to develop calendars. Their knowledge of the recurrence of the seasons for agriculture and of reference points in the sky for navigation was essential for a developing culture.

Other ancient civilisations, such as the Egyptians and the Chinese, had impressive constellation maps, and developed schemes for tracking the motions of the Sun and the Moon in their attempts to solve the problem of how the Moon's motion was synchronised with the Sun's. Though the Moon provides a very convenient time cycle for dividing up the year, it has no bearing on the all-important seasons, which depend on the Sun.

The Babylonians went further than others in their efforts to use the Moon's cycle as a universal timekeeping device. They did this by studying the motion of the Moon as it orbits the Earth. Their observations were accurately and systematically recorded over long periods of time. Next, they searched their records for repeating patterns of the Moon's motion, such as the phases it passed through in the course of a month, and the succession of positions on the horizon where it rose and set. Finally, they simulated these patterns using mathematical models to predict future positions. All this bears a surprising similarity to modern applied mathematical science. It may be hard to believe, but this is how the Babylonians studied the motion of the Sun and the Moon over three thousand years ago.

CELESTIAL OMENS AND DIVINATION

However, developing a lunar–solar calendar was relatively simple compared with their deeper goal. Their aim in studying the motions of the Sun and Moon was actually to gain a complete understanding of the movements of these primary heavenly bodies. The astronomer-priests would then be able to anticipate, as much as possible, the appearance of a lunar or solar eclipse, the most fearful omens in the sky. An eclipse of the Sun or Moon was an awesome sight for the ancients. There is much evidence from early societies that they were profoundly disturbed by the darkening and disappearance of the two celestial bodies which seemed to govern and sustain their existence.

By the third millennium BC, the Babylonians had become obsessed with celestial omens, eclipses in particular. As a result these heavenly phenomena had assumed a central position in their religious beliefs. Unlike the Egyptians, who had little interest in the dozens of solar eclipses whose paths crossed the Nile during this same period, the Babylonians were so concerned about eclipses of the Sun and the Moon that they developed elaborate schemes to record these events over very long periods of time. This kind of record-keeping is very similar to our own. In fact, many have said that the Babylonians were the fathers of astronomy. However, while their methods of observing and record-keeping were similar to our modern applied mathematical astronomy, their motivations were very different. As J. J. Finkelstein has explained:

> To the Mesopotamian, the entire objective universe was the crucial and urgent study, without any interposition of the self between the observer and the observed ... There

probably has never been another civilization so single-mindedly bent on the accumulation of information, and on eschewing any generalization or enunciation of principles.

The Babylonian quasi-religious belief in divination is an unexpected place to start a search through history for the origins of astronomy. Divination was an attempt to determine the will of the gods. To the Babylonians this was the same as an attempt to predict a future event. They believed themselves to be constantly surrounded by a host of evil spirits who caused insanity, sickness, accidents and death. To protect themselves against these spirits, they wore charms, put the image of a god at their doors and had magicians recite incantations. In addition, they depended on an elaborate hierarchy of priests who offered supplication to the gods. This was not idle superstition, but an important part of Babylonian philosophy: they believed that their very destiny was in the hands of the gods. They also believed, surprisingly, that their destiny was negotiable.

Divination rites were a way to communicate with the gods, to determine their will and perhaps change it. The discovery of signs from the gods, usually found in nature, was the first step in this process. As early as the third millennium BC they practised extispicy, the reading of the entrails of animals for clues from the gods to the nature of disasters to come. A sheep's liver was commonly used for this practice. Extispicy was studied for centuries in the temple schools of Babylonia.

Considered as an act of religion, extispicy was an attempt to consult with the gods, to placate them, obtaining their cooperation and learning of their future intentions. The Babylonian gods were 'sympathetic', and might choose to change the divine decree, as a human king might. In addition to the entrails of sheep, the priests looked for clues to their fate in the behaviour of birds and other animals, the path of smoke from incense and the patterns of oil on water. We can look upon these divinations as the forerunners of readings of tea leaves settled in the bottom of a cup.

At some point in their history the Babylonians began to look to the heavens, thought to be the home of the gods. They sought their destiny in unusual celestial happenings – and there is none more unusual than an eclipse. Strange omens in the heavens, like strange patterns in the entrails of sheep, were not the cause of impending disaster but a warning intended to elicit the appropriate ritual of supplication. But this transition from extispicy to the birth of archaic astrology did not take place overnight. For example, a letter from a diviner from the time of Hammurabi in about 1780 BC reported on an eclipse of the Moon which he suspected was a bad omen. However, the letter shows that he was not yet confident in the new celestial form of divination. So in addition to celestial observation, the diviner also checks out the omen by means of extispicy.

Nevertheless, the practice of divination-astrology was growing. For example, a short manual of celestial omens that appeared during Hammurabi's dynasty contained the following instruction,

Figure 2.2. Nineveh, capital of Assyria, the walled city on the Tigris.

'If, on the day of its disappearance, the god Sin [the Moon] slows down in the sky [instead of disappearing suddenly], there will be drought and famine.' Although celestial omens were beginning to be studied during the Old Babylonian period, the real development in the observation of the heavens came later, in the first millennium BC, in the time of the Assyrian empire.

The Assyrians were an extremely warlike people who lived around Assur in the Tigris Valley. They had discovered the secret of smelting iron to make weapons, iron being a tougher metal than the bronze used by the Babylonians. With this advance they

49

initiated a series of great and often cruel wars in the early part of the first millennium BC, destroying the first Babylonian state and extending their boundaries towards Asia Minor and Armenia. The new capital of the Assyrian empire was Nineveh. The political centre of a large military empire, the city was adorned with magnificent buildings, all made of the ubiquitous clay. As a great and rich commercial centre only a few hundred kilometres from Nineveh, Babylon initially retained its rank as a venerable seat of ancient culture. However, in 689 BC the Assyrians turned against the great city and had it destroyed. Even the mudbanks controlling the Euphrates were broken, flooding much of the city and turning the area into a swamp.

The Assyrians had adopted from the Babylonians the ancient and quasi-religious practice of 'divination', and absorbed the methods of observation and recording the movements of the Sun and Moon carried over from the Old Babylonian period. Their rulers also began to employ specialists in divination to continue the tradition of recording and interpreting eclipses, conjunctions of the Moon with planets, planetary movements, meteors and comets.

Having taken up the Babylonian philosophy of divination and developed their own astrology, the Assyrians applied their skills of organisation and discipline to the systematic observation of the heavens. They began to build astronomical observatories with temple towers all over the region. Thus began a programme of heavenly omen collection previously unknown in the ancient world.

Reports that have come down to us from the period 709–649 BC indicate not just detailed observations, but, in the case of unfavourable eclipses, attempts at prediction. As the divination cult decreed, a successful prediction might provide the opportunity to make supplication to the gods against the expected danger.

While Assyria spread its kingdom by death and destruction as far as Asia Minor, parts of Persia and Egypt, the priests and scribes at Nineveh advanced the astronomical cult inspired by the sacred rites of divination. Over the hundred and fifty years of the empire's predominance, a wealth of observations and predictions were recorded and collected in the great library at Nineveh. The library had been built by the Assyrian king Assurbanipal to store over twenty-two thousand clay tablets. Hundreds of reports were sent from the observation stations to the king's palace. A cuneiform tablet of this period records that, 'The King has given me the order: watch and tell whatever occurs, so I am reporting to the King whatever seems to me to be propitious and well portending and beneficial for the King, my Lord can know.'

Eventually, the harshness and cruelty of the Assyrians drove their subjects to revolt. They were attacked by the Medes from the north and the Chaldeans from the south. After a terrible siege the great capital of Nineveh was taken by storm (612 BC) and the great library was destroyed. The Assyrian empire, which had dominated the Fertile Crescent between the Tigris and the Euphrates for a century and a half, was gone. Nevertheless, it is one of the ironies of ancient history that only because the great library was completely destroyed were the clay tablets preserved. They were buried under the collapsed walls of the library.

After the defeat of the Assyrians, power passed into the hands of the Chaldeans. They revived the old capital of Babylon as the centre of their empire. To historians of science, the Chaldeans are known in particular for their obsession with celestial observation and prediction which they inherited from the Babylonians. There are conservative estimates that these people observed 373 solar eclipses and 832 lunar eclipses during their history, an impressive record given the rarity of these phenomena.

During the period of Assyrian domination, from the succession of the Chaldean King Nabonassar in the middle of the eighth century, precise historical records were systematically kept for the first time. Alternatively, as legend has it, Nabonassar destroyed all the records of the previous kings of Babylon so that the reckoning of the Chaldean dynasty would begin with him. This new beginning was so effective that, centuries later, Ptolemy, the Greek astronomer and geographer, could only begin his historical account of the Babylonian kings from this date, even suggesting that the era began at midday on 26 February 747 BC.

This day also marks an important beginning in the history of astronomy, because from here on the Chaldeans recorded highly accurate astronomical observations on a regular basis. Though it is true that the motive for these records was still mainly astrological, the observations became increasingly what can only be described as scientific.

THE ECLIPSE ARCHIVE FROM BABYLON

The astronomical texts, records of observations and predictions, reveal that through centuries of pre-eminence under the Chaldean dynasties, and even during later periods of decline, celestial observations continued to be made at Babylon on a regular basis and with little change of pattern. Modern scholars estimate that the programme lasted almost eight hundred years, until after the time of Christ. The most recent surviving astronomical text dates from AD 75, an almanac prepared from contemporary observations. Thus, from 750 BC to AD 75, there exists an archive of what the observers of Babylon saw in the heavens and recorded on clay tablets.

To put this achievement into perspective, consider an equivalent project to make similar observations at Windsor Castle, starting at about the time of the castle's construction in the early thirteenth century. This was the time of Richard the Lionheart and the Magna Carta. If the continuity of the Windsor 'archives' were to match Babylon's, the skywatching would still be going on today, as the twentieth century gives way to the twenty-first. The observations would have continued through the reign of the Plantagenets and the War of the Roses, Elizabeth and the Spanish Armada, the Civil War and the Restoration. Perhaps in the late seventeenth century the observations would have been taken over by the Astronomer Royal, and examined by Isaac Newton and Edmond Halley. During Victoria's reign the project would no doubt have been supervised by Prince Albert, science enthusiast

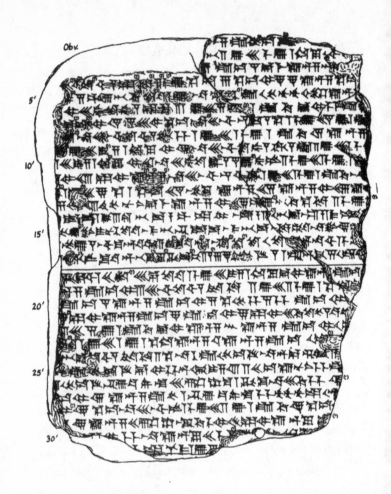

Figure 2.3. A Babylonian cuneiform text: an astronomical diary from 164 BC
(British Museum).

and overseer of great civic works. Finally, in the twentieth century, astronomer-priests would get deferments from the Great War, survive the blitz of the Luftwaffe and even the celebrations marking the dawn of the new millennium.

The priests and scholars responsible for this remarkable coordinated programme have been called the Babylonian watch-keepers. Their main motive for skywatching at Babylon was no doubt astrological; they generalised the observations to produce almanacs that were used for astrological predictions. Nevertheless, as the centuries passed and mathematical models were applied to reproduce past observations and predict future movement of celestial bodies, the cult of astrology came more and more to resemble astronomy.

DISCOVERIES OF LATE BABYLONIAN ASTRONOMY

Another aspect of the Chaldeans' astronomy was their ability to use their extensive catalogue of celestial observations. While the watch-keepers continued to search the heavens for omens, astronomers were able to develop a mathematical theory from their study of the records. Their analysis of the records of ancient observations suggested the possibility of creating models of the movement of the Sun and the Moon. From these models, astronomers would then be able to predict future astronomical phenomena. Once they had seen this possibility, the Chaldeans realised that they needed better accuracy in their observations. As early as 1000 BC their scribes had recognised eighteen constellations, groups of stars forming recognisable patterns in the sky. By 500 BC these constellations were systemised and identified, singly or sometimes in pairs, with the twelve lunar months as the Moon, Sun and the planets moved through the sky. For example, the second month of the Babylonian year, corresponding to mid-April to mid-May, had symbols of both Taurus and the Pleiades; the third month, Gemini and Orion; and the twelfth month, Pisces and Pegasus.

In order to introduce firm delineations for the purposes of astronomical diaries and observations, the ecliptic path along which the Sun moves was divided into twelve equal parts of 30°. This was called the zodiac, from the word for 'animal' – most zodiacal figures are animals or people. The first evidence of the use of this zodiac in a diary is from 464 BC, and by about 400 BC the zodiacal constellations had been clearly defined, beginning with Aries for the first month, corresponding to mid-March to mid-April. This system of zodiac constellations has lasted essentially unchanged to the present day, both for the science of astronomy and the pseudoscience of astrology.

We might expect that for chroniclers who recorded every solar and lunar eclipse over many centuries it would be natural to look for patterns. This would have given them a means of predicting the most ominous happenings in the heavens. But it wasn't until the Hellenistic period, from the fourth century BC onwards, that the Chaldean astronomers began to use previous reports and diaries to look for repeating cycles.

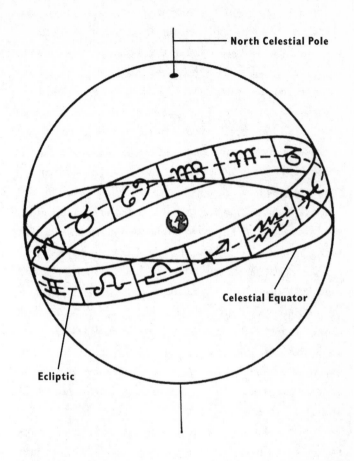

Figure 2.4. The zodiac: a belt of constellations along the ecliptic, originated by the Babylonians.

From their study of previous eclipses the astronomers were able to collate a set of rules for the prediction of lunar eclipses. They noticed that lunar eclipses never occur within six months of one another. They also discovered that if two lunar eclipses occur six months apart, they will be followed by a third lunar eclipse six months later. This happened quite often. If a lunar eclipse does not occur in an expected series, it could have occurred during daytime when the Earth's shadow on the full Moon would not be noticed. Thus the series is not broken, and another eclipse may occur six months later. If a lunar eclipse is observed a year or more after the last, and one month earlier than would have been expected on the basis of the last series, by then broken, it represents the first eclipse in a new series.

The short series described by these guidelines form part of a larger pattern of 18 years' duration. Within that 18-year cycle there are five such short series, followed by a sixth series which closely resembles the first. This begins a new 18-year cycle. Using these guidelines, an 18-year cycle for lunar eclipses was discovered. This cycle is called a saros, a Babylonian word meaning 'repetitive' though the Babylonians themselves did not use the word in this context.

A cycle of lunar eclipses is naturally easier to discover than a cycle of solar eclipses. There is a very simple reason for this: a lunar eclipse, which happens when the Earth's shadow falls on the Moon, can be seen from every point on the Earth's surface from where the Moon is above the horizon. Solar eclipses are seen less frequently.

Yet given that a lunar and a solar eclipse often occur a fortnight apart, it seems probable that the Chaldean astronomers of the fourth century BC may have guessed that an 18-year cycle also existed for solar eclipses. There is another theory of how they might have discovered it. This is shown in Table 2A, which lists certain solar eclipses observed by Assyrian astrologers in

Table 2A. Solar eclipses recorded at Nineveh, 744–635 BC.

	Date	Magnitude	Time
	744 Dec 9	0.80	11.58
	733 May 15	0.22	13.12
	717 Dec 10	0.56	16.10
	711 Mar 14	0.66	11.78
54 years	705 May 5	0.46	18.76
	704 Oct 19	0.86	13.54
	702 Mar 5	0.68	11.66
	695 Oct 10	0.36	09.07
	691 Jul 28	0.53	18.35
	690 Jul 18	0.29	09.38
	689 Jan 11	0.83	12.22
	679 Jun 17	0.68	07.41
	662 Jan 12	0.97	16.81
	661 Jun 27	0.93	16.75
	657 Apr 15	0.84	11.09
	651 Jun 7	0.72	12.50
54 years	650 Feb 21	0.93	16.07
	648 Apr 6	0.77	11.33
	641 Nov 11	0.86	10.53
	637 Aug 29	0.61	18.18
	636 Aug 19	0.67	08.68
	635 Feb 12	0.88	11.38

the seventh and eighth centuries BC. The magnitude of an eclipse is the fraction of the Sun's diameter that is covered by the Moon. It can be seen from the dates that all these solar eclipses have a previous eclipse predecessor 54 years earlier.

Once this pattern was noticed, it could be guessed that the number 54 might be a combination of a smaller series within the 54-year cycle, like 2 x 27 years or 3 x 18 = 54. (The reason why the Babylonians could observe a 54-year cycle directly at the same longitude but not an 18-year cycle is explained in the next chapter.)

However, the most important achievement of this entire effort from the standpoint of the history of science was the Babylonian solution to the problem of the motion of the Sun and the Moon. This solution undoubtedly grew out of problems associated with the development of the calendar. It was the Babylonians' custom to define the beginning of each month as falling on the day after the new Moon when the lunar crescent first appears after sunset. Originally this day was determined by observation, but later they wanted to calculate it in advance. However, by about 400 BC they had sufficient numbers of observations of the motions of the Sun and the Moon through the zodiac to know that these bodies did not have a constant speed. They appeared to move with increasing speed for half of each revolution, to a definite maximum, and then to decrease in speed to a measurable minimum.

Today it is known that the gravitational pull of an attracting body on an orbiting body produces a characteristic elliptical orbit in which the moving body is always speeding up or slowing down. The Babylonians attempted to represent this cycle arithmetically by giving the Moon a fixed speed for its motion during one half of its cycle, and a different fixed speed for the other half. Later they refined the mathematical method by allowing the speed of the Moon to increase steadily from minimum to maximum during one half of the cycle, and then to decrease to the minimum in the other half of the cycle.

With their calculations of the lunar and solar months, Babylonian astronomers could predict the time of new Moon and the day on which the new month would end. They would know the daily positions of the Moon and the Sun for every day during the month. This was a true mathematical science, which reached the height of its creativity during the Seleucid period in the second century BC, when the astronomers moved away from the ancient city of Babylon. It was now possible to reduce the predictions of celestial basics to mathematical models and not to rely heavily on observation. Though this led to highly precise predictions, the Babylonians surprisingly never formulated any geometrical model of the cosmos which might have supported their calculations. Instead, the problems were solved arithmetically without recourse to a cosmology of the type developed by the Greeks; that would follow only when Babylonian and Greek astronomy were linked after the conquests of Alexander the Great.

Through further studies, the Babylonian scribes had learned to produce ephemerides – tables of the future positions of the

Sun, the Moon and the planets. So, in addition to the systematic records of careful observations available to them, the scribes made use of their sexagesimal number system and their knowledge of mathematics to take full advantage of the cycles revealed by their observational records. Once the ephemerides were completed, the astrologers could make predictions even without the observations, and in all kinds of weather. The importance to the future of astronomy, meteorology, navigation, and the like of this new mode of providing written, predictive information hardly needs to be emphasised.

THE DECLINE OF BABYLON

During this period of astronomical development, the Chaldean dynasty lost control of political power in Babylon. After less than a hundred years their empire was overthrown by a powerful alliance of Medes and Persians in 538 BC, and Babylon became part of the Persian empire under Cyrus the Great. The days of independent Mesopotamian kingdoms were over. But still the astronomical observations continued.

During more than two centuries of Persian rule, Babylonian astronomy continued to improve in the accuracy of observation and mathematical prediction. Then the city of Babylon again shifted its political allegiance. In 330 BC the Persians were conquered by the armies of Alexander the Great, beginning one of the most significant periods of cultural diffusion in history. It became known as the Hellenistic period. Alexander had planned to restore some of the glory of Babylon by making the city his eastern capital. Unfortunately, he died there only seven years later in the palace of Nabuchadnezzar II, in 323 BC. Within fifty years of Alexander's death the Greek ruler Antiochus I ordered much of the population of Babylon to move to the newly founded metropolis of Seleucid, 100 km to the north. The old city never recovered from this transfer of its intellectual and political core, though Hellenistic rule continued there well into the second century BC. At Seleucid, Babylonian astrology was replaced by a highly advanced form of Greek astronomy. One aspect of the development included Aristarchus of Samos' hypothesis that the apparent daily motion of the sky could be explained by assuming that the Earth turns on its axis once every twenty-four hours and, with the other planets, revolves around the Sun. This heliocentric explanation was rejected by most contemporary Greek philosophers, who could not believe that a big heavy Earth could revolve around the light bodies in the heavens. The geocentric system, bounded by the celestial sphere, would remain virtually unchallenged for two thousand years.

Thus ended the two-thousand-year Babylonian cultural development of watching the heavens. It had started with a concept of divination which inspired an obsession with observation and record-keeping of celestial omens. This led to mathematical simulation and the discovery of the saros series, which provided a method of predicting when an eclipse would take place. In Babylonian astronomy we have a model for scientific progress. Though it originated with the superstitious beliefs of astrology, it grew into a methodology that we can now see as foreshadowing the concepts and procedures used in the scientific world today.

The marriage between astrology and astronomy has had a strange history. There is no question that during the Babylonian era the motivation for this vast accumulation of celestial data was to satisfy the demands of rulers and general population alike for astrological divination. For many hundreds of years, particularly during the late first century BC, these data were obtained more and more by scribes and priests who could only just be described as astronomers.

The Babylonians were never attracted to the form of astrology popular today, which is based on the Greek geometric cosmology in which the celestial-sphere model and the zodiac provide a framework in which interpretations of personality traits for horoscopes and birth charts are drawn from ancient myths and legends. With Babylonian astrology, celestial configurations were not the final word: there was still hope that unfavourable events foretold could be avoided. Such a philosophy was therefore quite different from the version of astrology inherited by today's practitioners from the Greeks.

The change from divination to the more recognisable Greek astrology was due mainly to the influence of two major writings from ancient Greece – Plato's *Timaeus* and Ptolemy's *Tetrabiblos*. Thereafter, classical astrology provided a naturalistic rationale for natal horoscopes, marking the split between astrology as divination (Babylonian) and astrology as science (Greek). Greek astrology eventually split off and grew into the science of astronomy. It is sad that this fact is not appreciated in a positive way by historians of science. No doubt this is a reaction against the popularity of the absurd claims of astrologers in interpreting birth charts and horoscopes which to the scientific mind are completely untenable.

There can be little doubt that, without the influence of astrology, astronomical observations would never have been made in the ancient world. Though today's astronomers and other scientists loathe the concept, they should admit that this absurd pseudoscience has made at least one positive contribution to the history of science.

THE EARTH'S ROTATION

It is interesting to see how scientists today make use of the Babylonian records in astronomical and geological studies. One example of this heritage is the new determination of the change in the rotational speed of the Earth. Who would ever have dreamt that the report by an astronomer-scribe of a solar eclipse observed at Babylon in 136 BC would allow a modern physicist to accurately measure the decrease in the spin rate of the Earth twenty-two centuries later? But this is exactly what has happened.

It is well established that the Earth's rotation is slowing down. This is happening because of the forces exerted by the Moon on the Earth through the ebb and flow of the tides. As the Earth's rotation rate decreases, there is a corresponding increase in the length of the day of 2.3 milliseconds per century. The goal of many archaeologists working in astronomy today has been to use ancient records of precise celestial events to get a measure of the rotation rate that is independent of any theory. An eclipse observed at a particular point on the Earth thousands of years ago could be compared to a present-day computer projection of that same eclipse assuming a uniform spin rate throughout time. Any difference in the two eclipse paths would require a correction to bring them into agreement. This correction would, it was hoped, corroborate the experimentally determined rate of slowing of the Earth's rotation.

F. R. Stephenson of Durham University has for several years been studying the eclipse records of the Babylonian astronomers as recorded on cuneiform clay tablets. In 1998 he was able to reliably fix an exact date in 136 BC when an eclipse was recorded at the ancient city of Babylon. He compared this record with a prediction of the path of the same eclipse made using modern computer techniques. For the calculation, he assumed that there was no slowing down of the Earth – that its spin rate twenty-two centuries ago was the same as it is today.

The result was an eclipse track which misses the ancient city of Babylon by a considerable distance. With no correction for the slowing down of the Earth, the eclipse track crosses the latitude of Babylon (32.5°N) at a longitude of 4.3°W, as shown in Figure 2.5. A correction needs to be made to bring the eclipse track back to Babylon, where it was observed, at longitude 44.5°E. This is a considerable correction, almost 50 degrees of longitude, and can be made with a great accuracy.

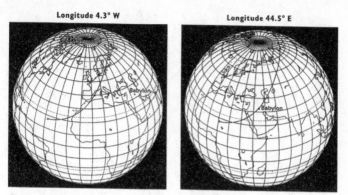

Longitude 4.3° W **Longitude 44.5° E**

Figure 2.5. Long-term changes in the Earth's rotation revealed by correcting the path of an eclipse observed at Babylon in 136 BC. The latitude of Babylon is 32.5°N.

The measured change gives an increase in the length of the day of 1.7 milliseconds per century. In other words, the Earth is not slowing down as fast as the theory of tides would predict, which is 2.3 milliseconds per century. There must be another component speeding up the spin rate of the Earth and decreasing the length of the day by 0.6 milliseconds per century. This component is thought to result from the decrease in the Earth's obliqueness, its flattening of its spherical shape, following the last ice age, and is consistent with recent measurements made by artificial satellites.

The thousands of dusty clay tablets in the British Museum, a product of our ancestors' attempts to placate the gods, may hold yet more secrets of ancient celestial configurations.

THE SAROS CYCLE:

THE 6585-DAY COINCIDENCE

There can be no living science unless there is a widespread instinctive conviction in the existence of an order of things.

Alfred North Whitehead

SCIENTISTS CONSTANTLY SEARCH for order. Reproducibility, predictability and simplicity are the ingredients of science. Though creative intuition, guess-work and luck all play a part, science consists mostly of cool, logical reasoning. Confronted with experimental observations that are too chaotic and have no discernible pattern, scientists tend to lose interest. They know that if any measurements they make on a physical system, such as the positions of a moving object, are not reproducible, the chances of them being able to apply mathematics to the measurements and get meaningful results are slim. ('Reproducible' means that they will find very similar values when they make the same measurements on another, identical system.) It is puzzling to most scientists why mathematics works in simulating orderly phenomena in the physical world. With disordered manifestations of nature, it would seem a miracle.

COUNTING THE DAYS

Figure 3.1 shows the paths of all the total and annular solar eclipses that occurred in the southern hemisphere from 29 May 1919 to 12 October 1939, as viewed from above the Earth's south pole. It is hard to see any order in these plots; the distribution is uneven and the paths have widely different lengths. This disorder is rather surprising. Eclipses are caused by the momentary alignment of the Earth and the Moon with the Sun during their continuous motion in predictable orbits. This motion is described by a simple set of laws and one single equation, Newton's universal law of gravitation. Regular orbital motion would imply a regular pattern of eclipses, an underlying order. But this is not apparent from the map.

The regularity is difficult to find. Nevertheless, it is there. As we saw in the last chapter, eclipses are related to others occurring about 18 years apart in a long series called a saros, a Babylonian word which means 'repetitive'. First used by a tenth-century Greek named Suidas to describe one of the Moon's periodic cycles, the word was later appropriated by Edmond Halley for the 18-year cycle of lunar eclipses discovered by the Babylonians in 400 BC. The seventeenth-century English astronomer, who was interested in classical writings, wished to honour the discovery made by these ancient people. Since Halley's time the term has been used for both solar and lunar cycles of the 18-year duration.

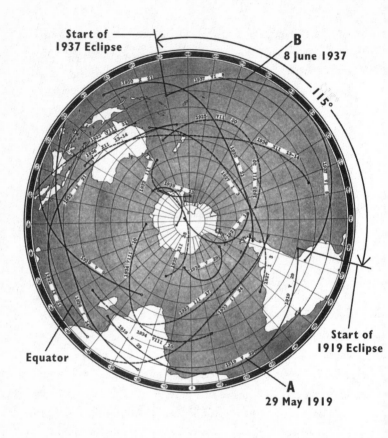

Figure 3.1. Total solar eclipses, 1919–1939, as viewed from above the south pole.

Since the total time period covered in Figure 3.1 is only 20 years, there can be only one or two pairs of eclipses plotted in it which are 18 years apart. One such pair of eclipses that belong to the same saros series has been marked on the map: A, the eclipse of 29 May 1919, and B, the eclipse of 8 June 1937. The characteristics of the two eclipses are similar. First of all, the two eclipse paths have a similar length and shape, though their starting points are shifted from each other by about 115° of longitude. The duration of totality and the width of the Moon's shadow are also similar for these two eclipses. This strongly suggests an underlying pattern of related eclipses in the same saros.

The exact time interval between these two eclipses can be found simply by counting the number of days between the two eclipses from 29 May 1919 to 8 June 1937. Leap years must be taken into account – 1920, 1924, 1928, 1932 and 1936 all have 366 days. The interval of 18 years and 10 days between the two dates amounts to 6,585 days. The question now is whether this 'magic' number of 6,585 days between consecutive solar eclipses has a deeper explanation.

Today, all the orbital details for the Moon and the Earth are known: their elliptical orbits, the rotation of the lines of nodes and the intervals between the different phases of the Moon. The reason why the saros exists can therefore be demonstrated. Furthermore, the relationship of one eclipse to another one in the same series can be explained, as can the latitude and longitude shift of consecutive eclipses in the same series. Finally, the progress of a saros series across the globe can be predicted, and the time span of a saros series and the number of eclipses it contains can be estimated. To do this it is necessary to recall some definitions from Chapter I concerning the various cycles of the Sun and Moon, and the concept of the ecliptic limit.

The saros results from a remarkable coincidence of nature, specifically with regard to the orbit of the Earth and the Moon. For no apparent physical reason, 223 synodic months (a synodic month being the time interval from one new Moon to the next) is almost exactly the same length of time as 19 eclipse years, an eclipse year being the time it takes for the Sun to travel from one passage through a node of the Moon's orbit, around the ecliptic, and back to the same node. The two necessary conditions for a solar eclipse to take place are that the Moon must be a new Moon and the Sun must be near a lunar node. The near equality of these crucial cycles ensures that the Sun and Moon will repeat their configurations. It is this equality that produces the saros cycle, the length of time between two related solar eclipses.

To determine the time period between two consecutive eclipses in the same saros, we need to multiply the relevant numbers together: 19 eclipse years of 346.62 days makes 6,585.78 days, while 223 synodic months of 29.53059 days (the accurate value) makes 6,585.32 days. The results are almost the same. The exact time between two consecutive saros eclipses is determined from the synodic month, new Moon to new Moon, since the eclipse occurs at new Moon.

There is one more very important relation in the saros cycle, and again it is coincidental. This is the fact that 239 returns of the Moon in its orbit from perigee to perigee (the point in its elliptical orbit where it is closest to the Earth), a period called the anomalistic month, also amounts to 6,585 days or, more precisely, 6,585.54 days. As a result, after one saros cycle the Moon is not only back to the same node, but also back to almost the same point in its orbit. The Earth–Moon distance will be almost the same as for the previous eclipse in the series. In terms of predicting the nature of successive eclipses in a particular saros cycle, the anomalistic month is almost as important as the synodic month. So at the end of 223 synodic months, the Moon is back to new Moon; at the end of 19 eclipse years, the Moon is back near its original position with respect to the node; and at the end of 239 anomalistic months, the Moon is back close to its original point in its orbit with respect to its distance from the Earth. Remarkably, to within a fraction of a day, these times are all the same. This explains why certain characteristics of the successive eclipses in the same saros are nearly unchanged – for example, the duration of the eclipse and the size of the Moon's shadow on the Earth.

All these cycles mesh together with almost the same 6,585-day period, causing solar eclipses occurring at 18-year intervals to have very similar characteristics. A large partial eclipse of the Sun will be followed by a large partial eclipse of the Sun, an annular eclipse by an annular eclipse, a total eclipse of short duration by a similar short total eclipse, and so forth. Detailed information on these cycles is given in Table 3A.

It remains to explain the significance of the decimal portion of the period of the saros, the odd 0.32 of a day. If the Sun

Table 3A. Cycles of the Sun and Moon showing similar saros periods.

Cycle	Description	Period (days)	Saros (cycles)	Period
Eclipse year	Time for Sun to complete a cycle from one lunar node to the same lunar node	346.62003	19	6,585.78057 back to lunar node
Synodic month	Time for complete cycle of phase of Moon as viewed from Earth (from new Moon to new Moon)	29.53059	223	6,585.32157 back to new Moon
Anomalistic month	Time for complete cycle of Moon around one orbit as viewed from outside the Solar System (from perigee to perigee)	27.55455	239	6,585.53745 back to perigee

were on the meridian, its highest point in the sky, at the middle of the eclipse, the eclipse would be at noon. After 6,585 complete days the Sun will be at the meridian again, but the new Moon will not yet have occurred. An additional 0.32 of a day must pass before a new Moon and the eclipse occur.

Within this 0.32 of a day, the Earth spins on its axis through an additional 32 per cent of a rotation. As one full rotation is 360° of longitude, this percentage is equivalent to the Earth having rotated about 115° of longitude to the west. This is apparent from Figure 3.1, where the 1937 eclipse is seen to have first touched the Earth about 115° west of the start of the 1919 eclipse. These two eclipses are related, belonging to the same saros cycle.

After a triple saros, or three cycles, 54 years and 33.96 days will have passed. The longitude shift corresponding to the extra fraction of a day is now 96 per cent of a rotation. So after a triple saros, the eclipse track does not begin until the Earth has rotated almost completely around to the same longitude. This can be seen in Figure 3.2, where the paths of the 1919 and 1937 eclipses have been transferred from a polar to a horizontal map projection. The path of the 11 July 1991 eclipse has been added to the map. The 1937 and 1991 eclipses are separated by a triple saros of 54 years and 33.96 days. It can be seen that the triple saros brings the eclipse back to nearly the same longitude. But though the 1991 eclipse path has about the same range of longitude values as in 1937, it has shifted north to higher latitudes. To explain this latitude shift, it is necessary to return to the concept of the ecliptic limit.

The Ecliptic Limit and the Saros Cycle

The periods of the various lunar cycles given in Table 3A and the diagram of the ecliptic limit from Chapter I are all that is necessary to understand the latitude shift and, indeed, nearly all the characteristics of a saros series of solar eclipses. The ecliptic limit is the maximum angular distance of the Sun from a node of the Moon's orbit at which a solar eclipse can occur.

In Chapter I we looked at a section of the ecliptic centred on a descending node (Figure 1.10), and saw that the angular spread of the ecliptic limit is always wide enough for the Moon to complete a synodic cycle while the Sun is within the ecliptic limit. Consequently, the Moon always catches up with and passes the Sun. This is the 'danger zone', since an eclipse will take place if a new or full Moon occurs within the ecliptic limit. Figure 3.3 is a similar diagram, and shows the sequence of solar eclipses in a saros cycle.

We follow the new Moon, starting with the critical positions at the western- and easternmost points. These end points of the ecliptic limit depend on the size of the image of the Sun and the Moon as seen from the Earth, as described in Chapter I. These sizes vary continuously because the orbits of the Earth and Moon are elliptical. As a result, the value of the ecliptic limit must also vary proportionally. The maximum ecliptic limit is called 'major' and the minimum ecliptic limit is called 'minor'. When the Moon is at perigee and the Earth is at perihelion, the Moon is closest to

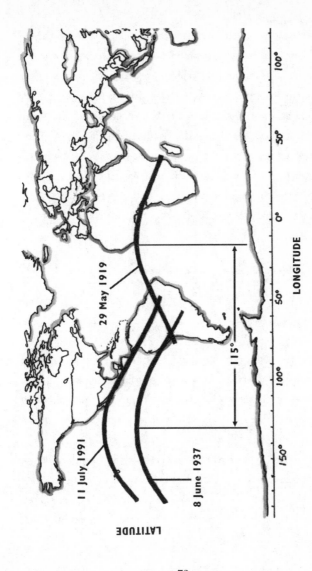

Figure 3.2. The shift of the path of a total eclipse for a single saros cycle (1919–1937) and a triple saros cycle (1937–1991).

the Earth and the Earth is closest to the Sun, and the solar and lunar disks are at their largest. This configuration gives rise to the major limit, as the two disks will appear to 'touch' sooner as the Moon approaches the node. When the Moon is at apogee and the Earth is at aphelion, the disks are at their smallest since the Moon is farthest from the Earth and the Earth is farthest from the Sun. This configuration gives rise to the minor limit, as the two disks will not appear to touch until the Moon is closer to the node. Table 3B gives the major and minor ecliptic limits for any type of eclipse, which are the same as the values calculated in Chapter 1, and for a total or annular eclipse.

Table 3B. Major and minor ecliptic limits for solar eclipses.

Type of eclipse	Major	Minor
Any solar eclipse	18.52°	15.35°
Total or annular solar eclipse	11.83°	9.92°

If the new Moon occurs outside the major ecliptic limit of 18.52°, an eclipse of the Sun cannot possibly take place. On the other hand, if the new Moon occurs within the minor limit of 15.35°, an eclipse must certainly take place. If new Moon occurs at a position between the two values, 18.52° and 15.35°, it is impossible to state whether an eclipse will take place or not without calculating the ecliptic limit using the appropriate orbital parameters. The conditions for a total or annular eclipse are found by using the major and minor ecliptic limits of 11.83° and 9.92° in a similar way.

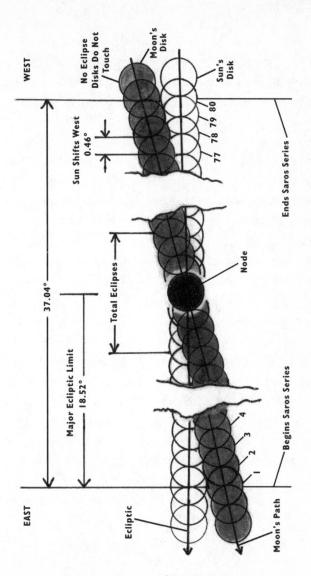

Figure 3.3. Eclipses in a saros series at a descending node for the major ecliptic limit.

In the general discussion of the saros that follows, the major ecliptic limit has been chosen; it is convenient to assume the disks of the Sun and the Moon to have their maximum size, with the Moon at perigee and Earth at perihelion. Also for convenience, we shall continue to consider the descending node. From Figure 3.3 it can be seen that in a saros series of eclipses taking place at the Moon's descending node, consecutive eclipse paths will fall progressively farther north. As the whole series proceeds, the eclipse tracks trace out paths which span the globe from south to north. Now it is possible to see why this happens.

Referring again to the periods of the different cycles in Table 3A, 19 returns of the Sun to the same lunar node – 19 eclipse years – are equal to 6,585.78 days, while 223 synodic months, new Moon to new Moon, amount to the slightly shorter time interval of 6,585.32 days. If, for a particular eclipse in a saros series, a new Moon were to fall exactly at the node, then after 18 years and 11.32 days the new Moon would arrive before the node was reached. In fact, it will occur sooner, by the time difference between 19 eclipse years and 223 synodic months: 0.46 of a day. The Sun moves eastwards about 1° per day along the ecliptic, so 0.46 of a day will be equivalent to about 0.46°. This results in a westerly shift of 0.46° from one eclipse to the next. The Sun will not quite make it back to the node before the new Moon and the eclipse occurs. Having started at the node, it will be in a position on the ecliptic 0.46° west of the node when the eclipse occurs. This is shown in

Figure 3.3. Accordingly, after each succeeding saros cycle the new Moon and the eclipse point will be found 0.46° farther west.

A series of eclipses in the saros are shown in Figure 3.3, starting at the eastern limit and moving westward by 0.46° after each saros cycle. In this diagram the drawings of the new Moons can also be thought of as drawings of the eclipses, since the eclipses fall exactly at new Moon, when the Sun and the Moon have the same longitude on the ecliptic as seen from the Earth. It is also helpful to identify certain aspects of the diagram before we go any further: the easterly direction of the motion of the Sun and Moon, indicated by arrows; the Moon's path, crossing the ecliptic from north to south at a descending node; the 0.46° westward shift of the new Moons within the ecliptic limit; and the locations of the node and the end points which show the first and last eclipse in the series.

It is now possible to find the total number of eclipses and trace their progressive changes as they pass through the saros cycle. According to the value of the ecliptic limit already found, if the new Moon falls within 18.52° of the node, an eclipse of the Sun may take place. If the node is the descending one, as in the diagram, the Moon's disk will be south of the Sun's at the beginning of the series. The first eclipse of the series will occur at the eastern edge of the ecliptic limit, at point 1 in Figure 3.3. It will be a partial eclipse, visible only from extreme southern latitudes near the south pole. After 18 years and 11.32 days the conditions will be nearly identical, but the new Moon, and the eclipse, will take place this time 0.46° west of the previous eclipse, and nearer the node, at point 2. This eclipse will be visible on the Earth a little farther north of the preceding one. This can be understood by considering the changing direction of the Moon's shadow. With each succeeding return, 3, 4, 5, and so on, the new Moon moves nearer to the node, and the path of the shadow across the Earth's surface moves farther north. These are all partial eclipses. When the new Moon eclipses the Sun within 11.83° of the node, the eclipses becomes total as this is the value of the major ecliptic limit and the Moon's disk is a maximum, since the Moon is at perigee. For the minor limit, annular eclipses would have begun to occur when the Moon reached 9.92°.

As with the partial eclipses, the total eclipse track will first touch only extreme southern latitudes, each succeeding eclipse moving farther to the north. Successive eclipses in the saros sequence will continue to be total until the new Moon reaches 11.83° west of the node, when the Moon's umbral shadow cone moves off the Earth's surface from the north polar region. A series of partial eclipses then follows until the Moon is 18.52° west of the node, when this particular eclipse cycle comes to an end, and the penumbral shadow of the Moon sails off beyond the north pole into space. If the eclipses had taken place at the ascending node of the Moon's orbit instead of at the descending node, the shadow cone would first have fallen on the Earth in the north polar region, and eclipses would have gradually moved southwards, the shadow cone going off the Earth from the south polar region.

SIZE AND DURATION OF A SAROS SERIES

It is also possible to estimate the number of eclipses in a saros series. Again referring to Figure 3.3, add the major ecliptic limit east of the node to the major limit for the west, to obtain 37.02° for the full range. If the new Moon shifts by 0.46° for each cycle, then the number of cycles that will fit in a major saros series can be found by determining how many westerly shifts are contained between the two major ecliptic limits. Dividing the angle 37.02° by the shift for each eclipse of 0.46° gives 80 saros cycles to a major series. A similar calculation can be done for the minor ecliptic limits: twice the minor limit of 15.35° makes 30.70° which, divided by 0.46°, yields 67 saros cycles to a minor series. A major series could thus last as long as 80 cycles of 18 years 11.32 days, which is 1,442 years. A minor series could be as short as 67 cycles, or 1,206 years. A saros series can be of any duration between these two limits.

The diagram of the eclipse paths at the beginning of this chapter, Figure 3.1, shows a confusing number of disconnected eclipse paths over a 20-year period in the early part of the twentieth century. We are now in a position to understand the distribution of these paths. First of all, every eclipse belongs to a particular saros series. However, the eclipses that take place within any given year obviously all belong to different saros series. In a comprehensive study, Theodor von Oppolzer (1841–86) found that solar eclipses occur at an average rate of 238 per century, or 2.38 per year. Thus 43 eclipses would occur on average during an 18-year saros cycle. Since, obviously, none of these can belong to the same saros, there must be 43 different saros series running in parallel at any given time.

All saros series begin with partial eclipses visible only from extreme latitudes, the south polar region if eclipses occur at a descending node, as we have been considering. These are followed by total and/or annular eclipses, depending on the major/minor ecliptic limit, each farther north than the previous one. The sequence ends with a group of partial eclipses near the north geographic pole. Figure 3.4 shows the paths of total eclipses belonging to the same saros cycle occurring at a descending node. These are polar views which can easily be compared with Figure 3.1. The view on the right is from above the south pole, and shows the paths of eclipses in the series that began on 12 July 1211. The paths can be seen to move towards the equator. The view on the left is from above the north pole, and shows paths moving from the equator up to the north pole, the series ending on 30 October 1986. These symmetrical paths, uniformly distributed around the poles, show that there is after all an orderly underlying pattern to the repeating saros cycle of eclipses originally discovered by the Babylonians 2,400 years ago.

SAROS 136

Eclipses belonging to the same saros cycle have similar characteristics because the coincidental repeating cycles return the Sun and Moon to nearly the same configuration after 6,585 days. To

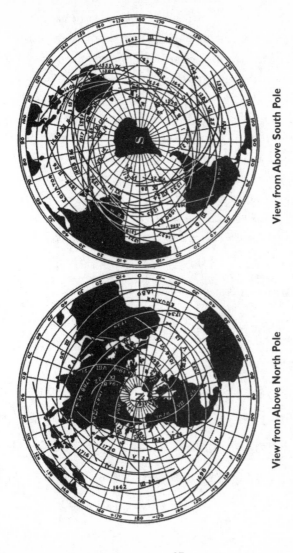

View from Above North Pole **View from Above South Pole**

Figure 3.4. A saros series of 44 total solar eclipses occurring at a descending node. The series began in the south polar region on 12 July 1211 and ended at the north polar region on 3 October 1986.

test these conclusions, we now examine a particular saros. Table 3C gives the date, the duration, the width of the maximum eclipse and the path location for all the twentieth-century eclipses in the saros family that has been given the classification number 136. (The numbering is based on the classification of saros cycles originated by the Dutch-Canadian astronomer Van Den Bergh in 1955.) The series has some of the longest eclipses in history and includes the great Baja Mexico eclipse of 1991, viewed by the author, and the 1919 eclipse, the quarry of the historic expedition to confirm Einstein's theory of general relativity, described in Chapter 7.

We can now analyse a specific saros series, Saros 136, as it progressed up the globe over a period of 1,262 years. The series

Table 3C. Characteristics of twentieth-century eclipses in saros series 136.

Date	Duration (mins)	Width (km)	Path of totality
18 May 1901	6:28	237	Indian Ocean, Sumatra, Borneo, New Guinea
29 May 1919	6:50	245	South America, Atlantic Ocean, Africa
8 June 1937	7:04	249	Pacific Ocean, Peru
20 June 1955	7:07	253	South-east Asia, Philippines, Pacific Ocean
30 June 1973	7:03	256	Atlantic Ocean, Central Africa, Indian Ocean
11 July 1991	6:53	257	Hawaii, Mexico, Central America, Brazil

began when a new Moon crossed the ecliptic near the limit of a descending node on 14 June 1360. Only a small part of Antarctica was touched by the penumbra that day. Eighteen years, 11.32 days later, on 25 June 1378, more of the Earth was within the penumbra as the eclipse path moved north. The first annular eclipse in this series occurred 140 years later, and on 17 January 1703 the first total eclipse took place. For the next eight hundred years eclipses sweep across the globe, including those listed in Table 3C for the twentieth century as the series moved nearer to the equator at the midpoint of the cycle, where we enjoy optimum conditions, as described above. The last total eclipse of the series is on 13 May 2496, and the final eclipse of all will be visible only near the Arctic circle as a partial eclipse on 30 July 2622. Table 3D lists the date and type of eclipse for each of the 71 eclipses in the Saros 136 series.

In 1991, for the Baja Mexico, eclipse, this series was almost precisely at its midpoint, the thirty-sixth in the series. This meant that it would be observed in the equatorial regions of the Earth. In these regions, eclipses are of long duration because the rotational speed at the surface of the Earth is greatest. Since the motion of the Moon's shadow and the rotation of the Earth are in the same direction, the rotation partially cancels out the speed of motion of the Moon's shadow. The twentieth-century eclipses of Saros 136 near the equator are therefore of long duration, close to the theoretical maximum of 7 minutes and 31 seconds. This can be seen from Table 3C; the eclipse of

Table 3D. Complete timetable of eclipses in saros cycle 136.

Date	Type	Date	Type	Date	Type
1360 Jun 14	Partial	1793 Mar 12	Total	2225 Dec 1	Total
1378 Jun 25	Partial	1811 Mar 24	Total	2243 Dec 12	Total
1396 Jul 5	Partial	1829 Apr 3	Total	2261 Dec 22	Total
1414 Jul 17	Partial	1847 Apr 14	Total	2280 Jan 3	Total
1432 Jul 27	Partial	1865 Apr 25	Total	2298 Jan 13	Total
1450 Aug 7	Partial	1883 May 6	Total	2316 Jan 25	Total
1468 Aug 18	Partial	1901 May 18	Total	2334 Feb 5	Total
1486 Aug 29	Partial	1919 May 29	Total	2352 Feb 16	Total
1504 Sep 8	Annular	1937 Jun 8	Total	2370 Feb 27	Total
1522 Sep 19	Annular	1955 Jun 20	Total	2388 Mar 9	Total
1540 Sep 30	Annular	1973 Jun 30	Total	2406 Mar 20	Total
1558 Oct 11	Annular	1991 Jul 11	Total	2424 Mar 31	Total
1576 Oct 21	Annular	2009 Jul 22	Total	2442 Apr 11	Total
1594 Nov 12 *	Annular	2027 Aug 2	Total	2460 Apr 21	Total
1612 Nov 22	Annular/Total	2045 Aug 12	Total	2478 May 3	Total
1630 Dec 4	Annular/Total	2063 Aug 24	Total	2496 May 13	Total
1648 Dec 14	Annular/Total	2081 Sep 3	Total	2514 May 25	Total
1666 Dec 25	Annular/Total	2099 Sep 14	Total	2532 Jun 5	Total
1685 Jan 5	Annular/Total	2117 Sep 26	Total	2550 Jun 16	Partial
1703 Jan 17	Total	2135 Oct 7	Total	2568 Jun 26	Partial
1721 Jan 27	Total	2153 Oct 17	Total	2586 Jul 7	Partial
1739 Feb 8	Total	2171 Oct 29	Total	2604 Jul 19	Partial
1757 Feb 18	Total	2189 Nov 8	Total	2622 Jul 30	Partial
1775 Mar 1	Total	2207 Nov 20	Total		

*1st date from the Gregorian Calendar.

1955, visible from South-east Asia and the Pacific, was one of the longest in history.

Now we can understand how the order of the heavens, not evident at the beginning of this chapter, comes about. There are 43 unrelated saros cycles in progress at any one time. When one series finishes and the shadow disappears, say away from the north polar regions of the Earth, the first eclipse of a new series just touches the south polar regions. Thomas Crump has used the metaphor of a Bach fugue in which the various melodies play out their themes in 1,206 or 1,442 years – the harmony of the spheres.

ANCIENT PREDICTIONS OF ECLIPSES: CONTROVERSIES

*I will be sufficiently rewarded if when telling it to others
you will not claim the discovery as your own, but say it was mine.*

Thales, sixth century BC

T WO QUESTIONS about the prediction of eclipses in the ancient world continue even today to cause controversy in academic circles. The first is whether England's famous megalithic stone circle at Stonehenge was ever used to predict eclipses. The second concerns the truth of the report by ancient Greek historians that the philosopher Thales predicted an eclipse of the Sun in the early part of the sixth century BC.

The opinion of the great majority of respectable historians, archaeologists and anthropologists today is that both these claims are false. In the first instance, critics argue that the very idea of such an advanced proto-science as eclipse prediction being practised by megalithic people is absurd, considering that they could not even write. Also, it is argued, the alignments of stones at Stonehenge which the theory's proponents believe were used in eclipse prediction are not accurate enough to track the exact position of the Moon in advance of an eclipse. In the second instance, the case against Thales rests on the fact that no historian of science today can figure out how he could have made the prediction. Therefore, it is argued, he didn't do it!

It is important to ascertain how eclipses could have been predicted at all by the ancients. The accomplishment would have to have been based on the discovery of a repeating cycle of eclipses. Alternatively, a repeating cycle of the Moon's motion might have been found and correlated with previous eclipses. Two such cycles have been discussed in this book: the 18.61-year cycle of the rotation of the Moon's line of nodes, and the saros cycle of eclipses, with a period of 18 years and 10 days. It is important not to confuse these two cycles, which have nearly the same period. They are completely unrelated. The claims for Stonehenge as a predictor of eclipses are based on the first of these cycles, the rotation of the nodes. The feasibility of Thales' prediction, as proposed recently by a Russian historian of science, is based on the second cycle, the saros.

STONEHENGE ASTRONOMY

The variation of the rising and setting points of the Sun and the Moon on the horizon surprises many people. The Sun doesn't simply rise in the east and set in the west. In northern latitudes like those of the British Isles, the Sun rises quite far north of east in summer, and sets well north of west. In winter, the Sun rises south of east and sets south of west. This is a result of the tilt of the Earth's rotational axis: in summer, the northern hemisphere leans into the Sun; in winter, it leans away from the Sun. The farther north an observer moves, the greater the difference between the rising and setting points of the Sun and Moon along the horizon.

Given this wide seasonal swing, it would seem natural for ancient observers at high northern or southern latitudes to have

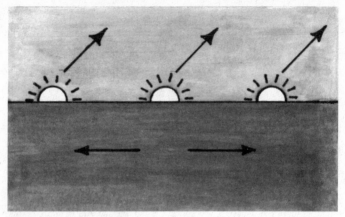

Figure 4.1. Horizon astronomy.

used 'horizon astronomy'. Calendars and almanacs can be devised by checking the motion of the Sun and Moon along the horizon rather than the shadow length of a post in the ground or the height of the midday Sun. Instead of watching the Sun at noon or the Moon at midnight, the Stonehenge people watched the rising and setting points on the horizon.

They would soon have noticed that the position at which the Sun rises on the eastern horizon oscillates back and forth between a northern and a southern extreme. These two extremes, known as the 'standing still' positions, are the points on the horizon where sunrise stops its motion along the horizon, turns, and starts to cycle back to the other extreme. These 'standing still' points for the Sun are marked at Stonehenge by principal alignments of the standing stones.

The Sun's motion is clearly all-important for dividing up the year and preparing a calendar. But not so the Moon. Yet it seems that those who built Stonehenge were also intensely interested in the Moon's motion. Was it to further sub-divide the year, or to predict eclipses? The full Moon's extreme positions on the horizon were also marked at Stonehenge. The variations of moonrise are even wider than those of sunrise. The alignments through the standing stones at Stonehenge to the extreme positions of the Sun and Moon are shown in Figure 4.2. The extreme swings along the horizon of the rising and setting of the full Moon take exactly 18.61 years. This includes the swings between the major 'standstills', a to a, and the minor 'standstills', b to b, within the 18.61 year cycle.

The realisation that the principal alignments in Stonehenge were with the extreme positions of the Sun and the Moon came about in 1965, when the British-born astronomer Gerald Hawkins, a professor of astronomy at Boston University, published *Stonehenge Decoded*. In this book Hawkins describes a computer analysis of the principal alignments of the viewing directions between the stones. He found that all the principal alignments pointed towards the extreme positions on the horizon of the rising and setting of either the Sun or the full Moon. In other words, Stonehenge was a megalithic astronomical observatory incorporating a calendar based on the Sun and the Moon.

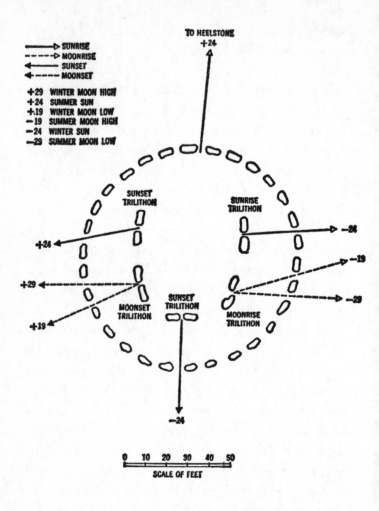

Figure 4.2. The principal alignments at Stonehenge (after Hawkins 1965).

The book caused a sensation among the *ancien régime* of archae-ologists — experts on the megalithic period who could not accept the attribution of an advanced technology to such an early society.

However, in what seemed to be a speculative elaboration of his computer work, Hawkins proposed that in addition to the principal alignments of the extremal positions of the Sun and Moon, Stonehenge was also used to predict eclipses. This was a radical idea which the British cosmologist Fred Hoyle further developed several years later. Hoyle proposed that Stonehenge was used to follow the positions of the lunar nodes around the ecliptic. When full or new Moon occurs near a node, the 'dan-ger zone', an eclipse can occur.

Obviously, if the cycle of the nodes was known, the Moon could be tracked very carefully to determine any relationship between the cycle and eclipses that were observed at Stonehenge. It seems that the builders were convinced that by accurately locating the extreme positions of the Moon, they could predict when an eclipse would take place. There are problems with this. The Moon moves about twelve times faster than the Sun through its extreme positions, and consequently the positions are more difficult to mark. Critics have argued that a much more accurate sighting system would be required than is avail-able at Stonehenge.

Because of the rotation of the line of nodes, the Moon swings back and forth between its extreme positions in the same

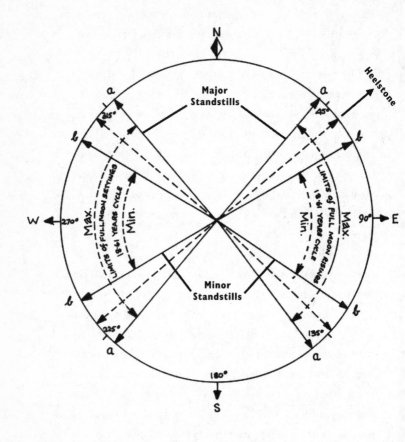

Figure 4.3. The cycle of the extreme horizon positions of the rising and the setting of the Moon at Stonehenge. The period of the cycle is 18.61 years. The letters a and b indicate the ranges of the major and minor standstills, respectively.

period as the nodal cycle. One result of this is the unusual movement of the winter full Moon near the central axis of Stonehenge, aligned with the marker known as the Heelstone, as shown in Figure 4.3. If the rising of the winter full Moon is studied for many years, and marked by sight lines, it will be found that its rising point swings back and forth across the Heelstone with a cycle of 18.61 years. When the full Moon rises in the centre of this swing, over the Heelstone, the point where the sun rises on the summer solstice, it is eclipsed.

It seems that the Stonehenge people were at least close to being able to predict eclipses. However, they have left no written records that might persuade scholars that the alignments at the site should be examined more closely. Unless the remains of an astronomer-priest are found in a megalithic tomb on Salisbury Plain with artefacts from this enigmatic structure, it is unlikely that the controversy over Stonehenge as an eclipse predictor will ever be settled.

EARLY GREEK ASTRONOMY AND SOLAR ECLIPSES

The claim that the Greek philosopher Thales (624–546 BC) predicted a solar eclipse in the sixth century BC is a different matter, for in this case there are many sources of information and speculation. Although no written works of Thales have survived, Greek historians such as Herodotus and Thucydides wrote extensively about his achievements.

*Figure 4.4. Thales (from a sculpture
at Hadrian's Villa, Tivoli).*

Thales, who came from the classical city of Miletus on the Ionian coast, was the first known Greek philosopher, scientist and mathematician. A figure of enormous prestige, Thales was the only philosopher who ranked among the Seven Wise Men of Ancient Greece. This was particularly significant because his status as a Wise Man came from his reputation as a philosopher, not from a position in politics, as was the case for the others accorded this honour. Some consider him to have been the teacher of Pythagoras, though it may be only that he advised Pythagoras to travel to Egypt and Chaldea. From Eudemus of Rhodes (about 320 BC) we know that Thales studied in Egypt and brought Egyptian learning to Greece. All ancient sources ascribe to him the introduction of mathematical and astronomical sciences into Greece. Since none of his writing survives, it is difficult to determine his philosophy and to be certain about his mathematical discoveries. Nevertheless, he is credited with five theorems of elementary geometry.

In spite of all his other achievements, Thales' fame has always rested on the reports of ancient Greek historians that he successfully predicted a solar eclipse. The most frequently quoted source is Herodotus. One of the most important writers of ancient Greece, Herodotus is often called 'the father of history'. In his famous chronicles of ancient Greek times, *The Histories*, he recounted the story of the war between the Lydians and the Medes. It was a long war which had been waged for five

Figure 4.5. A solar eclipse in the sixth century BC stops a battle between the Lydians and the Medes.

years with neither side gaining prominence. Herodotus tells how, during a battle on 28 May 585 BC,

> the day was turned to night. Thales of Miletus had foretold this loss of daylight to the Ionians, fixing it within the year in which the change did indeed happen. So when the Lydians and the Medes saw the day turned to night they ceased from fighting and both were more zealous to make peace.

It is wonderful to think that a war could be ended by a spectacular natural phenomenon which humbles belligerent armies, as the drawing shown in Figure 4.5 tries to capture. But more interesting to us today is Thales' prediction. How did he do it?

Some sceptical scholars have pointed out that the writings of ancient historians, Herodotus included, contain examples of portentous eclipses which never took place – now referred to as 'literary eclipses'. One report in Herodotus describes how Xerxes and his Persian armies observed an eclipse just before they set out from Sardis to conquer the Greeks. But no such eclipse can be found by modern computations to match the date of the invasion. Clearly, there was a political motive for creating a celestial omen: it would indicate that the gods were with Xerxes and a great change was about to take place. But Thales could have had no political motive for making an eclipse prediction. In fact, Thales' prediction may have been the real event that inspired other, fictional accounts.

It is not only Herodotus who tells us about Thales' eclipse prediction. Diogenes Laertius, in his *Lives of Eminent Philosophers*, refers to Xenophanes as having been amazed by Thales' achievement. This is significant since Xenophanes lived in the same century as Thales, and could therefore be a more reliable source. Nevertheless, respected modern scholars, Thomas-Henri Martin in the nineteenth century and Otto Neugebauer more recently, have concluded that the story of the prediction is nothing but a myth. It could be argued that such scepticism is unfair when viewed in the light of the usual procedures used in classical studies. Evidence from independent sources for Thales' prediction seems too strong to be denied. Yet, if we are to accept the reality of Thales' achievement, there remain the questions of how and why he made his prediction.

In 1994 Dmitri Panchenko of the Academy of Sciences in St Petersburg published a paper in the *Journal of the History of Astronomy* in which he attempted to solve this controversy among modern scholars. In his opening paragraph, he sets the scene:

> The prediction of a solar eclipse by Thales is one of the most celebrated events in the history of Greek science. It astonished his contemporaries and it has astonished modern scholars. Unfortunately, we have no ancient account of the method that facilitated Thales' extraordinary achievement, and all modern attempts at the reconstruction of such a method seem to have failed.

It has been argued that any reliable prediction of a solar
eclipse was impossible before the time of Hipparchus,
more than four centuries later.

Panchenko reviews all the reasons for dismissing the claim,
including the fact that the method used by Thales for his prediction has never been substantiated. He accepts that there was
a tradition at the time to credit famous men with discoveries
they did not make. Furthermore, he is not daunted by the fact
that most of today's historians of science treat the story as
apocryphal. In spite of all this, he sets out to show the feasibility of Thales' prediction.

The first approach would be to assume that Thales knew of
the saros cycle of 223 synodic months or 6,585.32 days. There
has been wide agreement among scholars that this was the
method he used for the prediction. But there is a problem here.
In the sixth century BC no such saros cycle was known for solar
eclipses at a given location on Earth because consecutive eclipses
in a saros cycle are separated by about 115 degrees of longitude,
one-third of the way around the world. Communications in the
sixth century BC being what they were, there is no way that
Thales could have known of solar eclipses which took place
that far from Ionia. Furthermore, the saros was not discovered
by the Chaldean astronomers until about 400 BC. So by this
argument Thales could not have used consecutive 18.61-year
saros eclipses as a basis for prediction.

Some scholars have suggested that Thales merely explained to the Ionians how an eclipse occurs, and declared that such a natural event was not at all dangerous and that it would probably reappear some time in the future. But this raises another problem. As eclipses were already known to the Greeks of this era, it seems unlikely that Thales' fame would result merely from his announcing that an eclipse *might* happen some time in the future. No, he would have had to do better than that. He would have needed to predict the date, or at least the year, of a particular solar eclipse.

Modern calculations of the dates of solar eclipses visible from Ionia during this period have allowed Panchenko to develop a plausible theory of why and how Thales predicted the solar eclipse. Panchenko agrees that Thales probably wanted to assure his compatriots that all was well in the heavens. He wished to emphasise that the series of three solar eclipses observable from Ionia within a few years of one another, listed in Table 4A, was a natural coincidence. To ease their anxiety further, Thales predicted when the next one would occur. It was quite unusual and indeed unsettling for three consecutive eclipses, the third of which was total, to be visible from the same location on Earth within the space of three years. The third eclipse in the sequence, that of 28 May 585 BC, must have been frightening for the Ionians. Considerably larger in magnitude than the two previous eclipses, its central path of totality crossed northern Anatolia.

Table 4A. Three solar eclipses visible from Ionia.

Date of Solar Eclipse	Magnitude (at Miletus)
29 July 588 BC	0.836
14 December 587 BC	0.835
28 May 585 BC	0.905*

*Total eclipse in northern Anatolia.

Though not particularly superstitious, the Ionian Greeks would have seen the Sun's light blotted out on three occasions in the space of three years, and must have been quite edgy. Both Plutarch and Thucydides reported anxiety among the Greeks at the times of eclipses. Plutarch tells a revealing story in his *Life of Pericles*:

> Pericles was commander of the Grecian naval forces and when the whole fleet was in readiness, and Pericles on board his own galley, there happened an eclipse of the Sun. The sudden darkness was looked upon as an unfavourable omen, and threw the sailors into the greatest consternation. Pericles, observing that the pilot was much astonished and perplexed, took his cloak, and having covered the pilot's eyes with it, asked him if he found anything terrible in that, or considered it a bad omen? Upon his

answering in the negative, he asked 'Where is the difference, then, between this and the other, except something bigger than my cloak causes the difference?'

According to Herodotus, Thales made a public announcement of his prediction, so it must have been at a gathering like the Pan-Ionian festivals, which were held every four years. Panchenko suggests that Thales was not so bold as to predict the exact date, but finds evidence in classical sources to support the estimate of the year: he said something like 'You will see a solar eclipse before our next festival.'

So, did this happen? There were two solar eclipses soon after which were visible from this region, on 21 September 582 BC and 16 March 581 BC. As the Greek year began at the summer solstice in June, both these eclipses would have been in the same 'calendar' year for the Ionians, 582/581 BC – the same year in which Thales received public recognition of his intellectual prominence by becoming the first Greek to be accorded the status of 'Wise Man'. This answers the 'why', and also the 'when'. But do we know 'how' the sage of Ionians predicted that the eclipses of 582/581 BC would occur before the next Pan-Ionian festival?

These were turbulent times in Greece and the ancient Near East. Just before the period in which Thales lived and worked in Ionia, the Assyrian kingdom was under continuous attack from the Chaldeans and the Medes, finally being destroyed during the period 626–600 BC. Major cities in Assyria, such as Nineveh, ceased to exist. It is likely that many of the empire's displaced intelligentsia – particularly trained astronomers and astrologers – would have emigrated to the court of the new power centre, Egypt. With the Assyrians, Egypt had a common enemy in the Babylonians. Politically, then, this was a time quite conducive to the spread of astronomical knowledge from Assyria to Egypt and then to Ionia.

It is not so far-fetched to imagine that Thales, a leading scribe from Ionia's most important city, may have met astronomers from Assyria in Egypt at the court of the Pharaoh Neccho (610–595 BC). There are many indications in other writings of Thales' travels to Egypt. In fact, Miletus had an important fortified maritime colony on the Nile delta. Thales, the originator of astronomy among the Greeks, could have learned of the eclipse records kept by the Chaldean priests and astrologers of Assyria in the seventh and eighth centuries BC. Now, the third and final eclipse in a triple saros of 54 years and one month can be seen from the same location as the last eclipse of the previous triple saros. Three shifts of the saros cycle brings the eclipse back to the original longitude, as indicated in Figure 3.2. The eclipses listed in Table 4B were recorded by Assyrian astronomers in Nineveh. This series of three triple saros cycles would enable Thales to predict the eclipse of 16 March 581 BC.

Table 4B. Three consecutive predecessors in the triple saros for an eclipse on 16 March 581 BC (from observational records at Nineveh).

Date of Eclipse	Magnitude
9 December 744 BC	0.80
54 years later:	
11 January 689 BC	0.83
54 years later:	
12 February 635 BC	0.88
54 years later:	
16 March 581 BC	prediction

It is possible that another cycle of 27 years was noticed first. For example, the following list of eclipses from Assyrian records are all separated by 27 years:

9 December 744 BC*
10 December 717 BC
11 January 689 BC*
12 January 662 BC
12 February 635 BC*

Those asterisked are, of course, separated by 2 x 27 = 54 years, the triple saros cycle. Also, the large gap after the eclipse of 2 February 635 BC would certainly have hinted at the triple saros cycle of 3 x 18 = 2 x 27 = 54 years.

Table 4C gives selected major solar eclipses observable at Nineveh in the period 689–635 BC, together with eclipses probably known to Thales, having been observed at Miletus. If all this information was made available to Thales through his Egyptian connections, his acceptance of a 54-year eclipse cycle is clearly probable. By comparing the two sets of eclipse data, Thales would have been able to establish a 54-year cycle, without knowing that it consisted of a triple 18-year cycle. The eclipse in 596 BC would have provided Thales with a crucial test for the continuity of the 54-year series. This eclipse was difficult to observe from Egypt or Babylon, but Thales could not have missed it from Miletus. It began at about 15:00, in the afternoon, and reached its maximum at 16:12, 38 minutes before sunset. The magnitude of 0.69 would have been quite enough to attract the attention of the inhabitants of Miletus.

Table 4C. Solar eclipses observed at Nineveh and Miletus, 689–635 BC.

Nineveh (observed by Assyrians)	Miletus (known to Thales)	Time difference (years)
12 Jan 662 BC	13 Feb 608 BC	54
15 Apr 657 BC	18 May 603 BC	54
7 Jun 651 BC	9 Jul 597 BC	54
21 Feb 650 BC	23 Dec 596 BC	54
6 Apr 648 BC	9 May 594 BC	54
11 Nov 641 BC	14 Dec 587 BC	54
12 Feb 635 BC	16 Mar 581 BC [†]	54

† Predicted by Thales

Dmitri Panchenko thus creates his case for Thales' prediction, based on the 54-year cycle, not of the eclipse of 28 May 585 BC, but of the eclipse of 16 March 581 BC, visible from Miletus. The hypothesis depends only on the quite reasonable assumption that Thales was acquainted with Eastern astronomy, and brings into agreement classical texts and the history of science. The date fits perfectly with Herodotus' testimony and with an independent report in Greek archives of the year of Thales' public recognition as one of the 'Seven Wise Men' of ancient Greece. There is still some confusion over the timing of the battle between the Medes and the Lydians which was halted by the eclipse, because another eclipse occurred at around the same time, 21 September 582 BC. Nevertheless, Panchenko seems to have answered the sceptics who would discard out of hand what seems to be a remarkable achievement for the sixth century BC.

The two well-known but controversial claims of eclipse prediction in the ancient world have quite different futures. Without any written records, research on the Stonehenge megalith has all but petered out and is unlikely to generate much interest in the future. Writing is the essential ingredient of any kind of scholarship. On the other hand, the debate regarding the spectacular claim in classical history of Thales' prediction of a solar eclipse has been reopened. Brilliant theorising by the Russian academician, Dmitri Panchenko, has produced a plausible explanation of a possible method used by Thales. Furthermore, the thousands of cuneiform records from Babylonian astronomers that survive on clay tablets date from hundreds of years before the Greeks. As contemporary research on cultural diffusion between ancient lands progresses, it may become clearer how Thales could have made his famous prediction. The lack of any explanation of how the prediction could have been made has hitherto been the great stumbling block for many contemporary historians. The Thales controversy can now be expected to have a lively future among science historians.

TRACKING A
SOLAR ECLIPSE

*Tho the Sun was be-clouded we were certain
it was not total there, as Dr. Halley then the
King's Astronomer had by his Map given ye
world to expect.*

James Logan, having tried
unsuccessfully to view the total
eclipse of 1724

ACCORDING TO THE FOLKLORE of the history of science, the bright, young astronomer Edmond Halley (1656–1742) was debating one day in a coffee shop in London's Strand with two of the finest scientists of the time, Robert Hooke (1635–1703) and Christopher Wren (1632–1723). They could not agree on the law governing the attraction between the Sun and the planets, and orbits of the planets around the Sun. After much argument and boasting, particularly by Hooke, they agreed that there was only one person who could settle the dispute, and Halley was elected to go to Cambridge to confront the great Isaac Newton. 'What kind of planetary orbit would result if the Sun's gravitational attraction obeyed an inverse-square law?' asked Halley. 'An ellipse,' replied Newton.

That one question, posed in 1684, set in motion a line of research that culminated in one of the greatest scientific achievements. Though Newton could not give Halley a proof of his statement at that first meeting, he promised to come up with the solution. Halley hoped that Newton would demonstrate mathematically what seventeenth-century scientists already thought was true. Most believed that the force of gravitation did obey an

Figure 5.1. Edmond Halley.

inverse-square law — that is to say, the attractive force between two bodies decreases as the square of the distance between them increases. If the distance were doubled, the force would reduce to a quarter of its original value; if the distance were trebled, the force would reduce to one-ninth of its value; and so forth. In addition, everyone knew from Kepler's laws that the planets moved in elliptical orbits. It was left to Newton to connect these two ideas.

Newton immediately expanded the scope of the question and produced a short monograph entitled *De moto corporum*, 'On the Motion of Bodies', which he sent to Halley. Excited by what he read, Halley asked Newton to expand the brief even further. Over the next two years Halley encouraged and pleaded with the temperamental recluse to exercise his genius. In an intense year and a half of calculating and writing, Newton proved not only that the inverse-square law is the cause of elliptical orbits of the planets, but by the time he had finished, he had solved nearly all the problems of celestial and terrestrial motion.

During this period Halley was Newton's therapist, calming him down after vitriolic written exchanges with others, especially his arch-rival Hooke. Realising more than anyone the importance of what Newton was creating, Halley arranged for the publication of the completed work, even making available some of his personal funds to meet the printing costs. The result was the *Philosophiae Naturalis Principia Mathematica* ('Mathematical Principles of Natural Philosophy') of 1687, perhaps history's single most important work in physical science. In his 'Ode to Newton' with which he prefaced the *Principia* (as it is usually called), Halley wrote, 'Nearer the Gods no mortal may approach.'

One application of Newton's new theory was a description of the elliptical orbit of the comet of 1682, which Halley had been studying. Using Newton's results, Halley discovered that this comet had the same orbit as one seen in 1607. Then he examined reports of a comet seen in 1531, and found the same orbit again. He announced that these 'different' comets were one and the same object, returning to the Earth's vicinity about every 76 years. Based on this orbital information, Halley predicted that the comet would be visible again in 1758.

Halley died in 1742, outliving Newton by fifteen years, but the world's astronomers did not forget his prediction. Yet when the appointed year arrived, there was mounting disappointment as almost the whole year passed without a sighting. Finally, on Christmas night, Johann Palitzsch, a Dresden amateur astronomer, became excited by an object he saw in the night sky. It was not the Star of Bethlehem but Halley's Comet, as it became known, returning to the inner Solar System from the far reaches of its elliptical orbit.

According to Harvard's historian of astronomy, Owen Gingerich, Halley was lucky to discover that the orbits of the 'three comets' were similar. The comet that bears his name is the only really bright one among the 140 or so periodic comets now known, and was therefore Halley's only chance of finding a returning comet without the use of a telescope. Though he did not live to see it, Halley has been justly immortalised for his discovery, a wonderful piece of detective work.

Halley was a man of many talents. He excelled in mathematics, astronomy and physics, and is considered to be the founder of geophysics for his early work on winds and tides. He was the first to establish an astronomical observatory in the southern hemisphere, on the island of St Helena, from where he cata-logued the southern stars. He was active in the Royal Society, for which he was secretary for many years. Later he undertook a variety of assignments for the Crown, including voyages to the South Atlantic to investigate magnetic compass bearings, and secret diplomatic missions to the court in Vienna. These activi-ties assured his election as Professor of Astronomy at Oxford, a position once held by his friend Christopher Wren, who had first set him on the road to Cambridge to ask for Newton's help. For the last twenty or so years of his life he served as Astronomer Royal, at Greenwich Observatory in London.

A BRIEF HISTORY OF ECLIPSE PATHS

One of Halley's lesser-known achievements was the prediction of the path of a solar eclipse in 1715 which crossed the south of England. This may have been the first time that the movement of the Moon's shadow across the Earth was computed. Certainly, we can take Halley's calculation as marking the beginning of mod-ern eclipse astronomy. In 1715 Halley managed to publicise his prediction of the eclipse path as a 'broadside', a single-page tabloid, that was hawked on the streets of London. He had his motives. In order to check his calculation of the path, Halley needed to collect reports from all around southern England. He had arranged for observations to be made from six points on the edges of the path of totality and from nine more within the umbra, including one from Greenwich Observatory.

Eclipse Path 1724

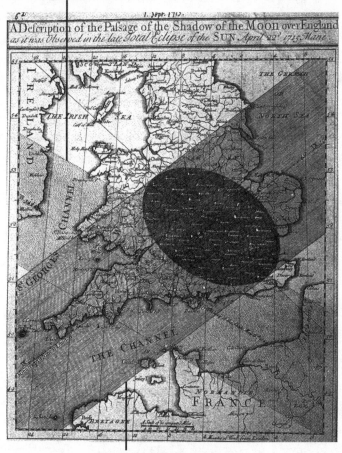

Eclipse Path 1715 (corrected)

Figure 5.2. Halley's predictions of the paths of the 1715 and 1724 English eclipses.

Figure 5.2 shows the path of the shadow of the Moon during the 1715 eclipse after being adjusted to conform with the reports of the observers. The white spots within the umbra indicate the locations of the monitors whom Halley had organised to record whether the eclipse was total. By comparing the monitors' observations with his computed values, Halley would be able to adjust his calculating procedure, thereby increasing the accuracy of future predictions. Given the rare occurrence of eclipses, it might seem that Halley was wasting his time. But he was aware of a remarkable fact: another total solar eclipse was scheduled to cross London in only nine years' time, in 1724. Halley would calculate its path with his refined procedure.

Others soon joined Halley in the attempt to compute the future paths of the Moon's shadow across the surface of the Earth. But such predictions remained an inexact art, and many would-be eclipse observers were frustrated by inaccurately calculated paths. A certain American, James Logan (1674–1751), was in London on a business trip at the time of the 1724 eclipse. Mixing business with pleasure, he decided to position himself in the path of totality, referring to Halley's map of the moving umbra. This was published in a broadside together with the corrected 1715 path, as shown in Figure 5.2.

By this time others were publishing broadsides on the eclipse, including Newton's successor as Lucasian Professor at Cambridge, William Whiston (1667–1752). The path predicted by Whiston differed from Halley's, but Logan chose to trust the more prestigious Halley, who by this time had been appointed Astronomer Royal. Logan made his way to Windsor Castle to view the eclipse, Halley's map in hand. But it seems that the Astronomer Royal had made a mistake. On the afternoon of 11 May 1724, the vast crowds of people who had journeyed from London to Windsor were disappointed. As Logan noted, 'Where we expected without fail to find it total, but tho the Sun was beclouded we were certain it was not total there, as Dr. Halley then the King's astronomer had by his Map given ye world to expect, and therefore this Map of W. Whiston's is by much the truest.' The question of who had the correct path, Halley or Whiston, was recently settled. Owen Gingerich has recalculated the two paths and shown that the actual edge of totality lay midway between Halley's and Whiston's published positions.

As a solar eclipse indicates exactly where the Moon is with respect to the Sun, this eclipse of 1724 allowed astronomers to improve the accuracy of lunar tables. These are tables that give the predicted positions of the Moon on the celestial sphere at any given time in the future. In the 1750s, when a great reward was on offer from the Crown for whoever could devise an accurate means of determining longitude at sea, these tables almost landed the prize. One solution of the problem, proposed by Nevil Maskelyne, then Astronomer Royal, was to determine longitude from lunar sightings aboard ship. Accurate lunar tables helped his case. However, the £20,000 eventually went to John Harrison for his invention of the marine chronometer. Nevertheless, the Longitude

Board awarded the widow of the Nuremberg map-maker Tobias Mayer £3,000 for his work on tables of lunar positions. Harrison came close to losing out to the lunar-distance method.

Not all stories of observers following eclipse predictions in the eighteenth century were as successful or uneventful as with Halley's or Whiston's. The Harvard professor Samuel Williams wished to observe the total eclipse of October 1780 from Maine, on the Atlantic seaboard of the United States. But there was a small problem. The War of Independence was in progress, and King George's troops had captured Maine. Nevertheless, with their sense of fair play and interest in scientific expeditions, the British allowed the Harvard expedition to sail into Penobscot Bay, which, Williams had determined, would be within the path of totality. A scientific 'truce' had been arranged for the eclipse observations to be made.

How dismayed the Harvard professor must have been when he arrived. He soon realised, after measuring the height of the noonday Sun, that he and his observing party were at the wrong latitude. The path of totality would pass about 30 km north of Williams' location. Sadly, the British commander had given him strict instructions not to move from the agreed position. In the short time remaining before the eclipse, there was no chance for Williams to renegotiate his observation point. It seems that calculations based on the above-mentioned Tobias Mayer's lunar tables, which had won the £3,000 for his widow, had led Williams to position himself below the actual southern limit of totality. Clearly, in the eighteenth century there was room for improvement in predicting eclipse paths. Maybe a machine could provide the answer.

THE ECLIPSAREON

Just about the time of the debacle of Penobscot Bay, a contraption had been developed in England to improve eclipse predictions, or at least to display the probable eclipse paths. The engraving reproduced in Figure 5.3 is from Chambers' 1779 *Cyclopaedia* and shows the Eclipsareon, whose sole purpose was to indicate the path of the Moon's shadow on the Earth during a solar eclipse. This was achieved by projecting the coordinate positions of the Moon and the Sun onto a screen. This screen, illuminated by candlelight, cast a shadow onto a rotating globe which mimicked the motion of the Earth. The various orbital parameters of the Sun, Moon and Earth were set mechanically. Then, when a crank was turned, the device would generate the entire path of the Moon's shadow during the eclipse. Precious artefact from that century of mechanical contrivances it may be, but the Eclipsareon was not very accurate. A detailed description of the Eclipsareon was given in the *Cyclopedia*:

> This is an instrument invented by Mr. Ferguson for
> submitting the time, quantity, duration and progress of
> solar eclipses at all parts of the Earth. The machine consists
> of a terrestrial globe turned by a winch and wrapped round

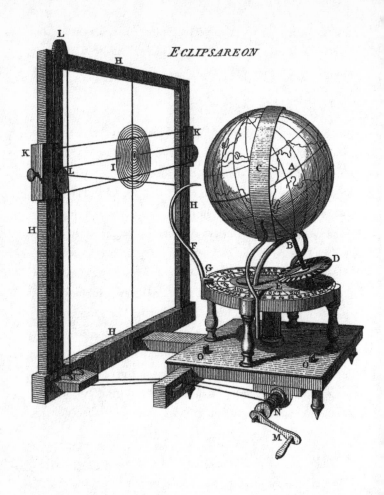

Figure 5.3. The Eclipsareon, 1779, for displaying the path of a total solar eclipse (see text for description).

its chassis B, inclined at 23.5 degrees and carrying an index round the hour circle D. A circular plate E on which the months and the days of the year are inserted and which supports the globe in such a manner that when a given day of a month is turned to the annual index G, the axis has its frame, positioned with the Earth's axis at that time. A wire F, points to the middle of the Earth's enlightened disk and shows to what place on the Earth the Sun is vertical at any given time. A penumbra, or thin circular plate of brass I, divided into 12 digits by 12 concentric circles and so proportioned to the size of the globe that its shadow, formed by the Sun, with a candle placed at a convenient distance with its rays transmitted through a convex lens can make them fall parallel on the ground, may cover those parts of the globe which the shadow and the penumbra of the Moon cover. An upright frame H, on the sides of which are scales of the Moon's latitude with two sliders K and K, fitted to them by means of which the centre of the penumbra may be always attracted to the Moon's latitude. A solar horizon C, dividing the enlightened from the darkened hemisphere and showing the places where the general eclipse begins and ends with the rising and setting Sun and a handle M which turns the globe round its axis by wheel works and moves the penumbra over the pulleys L with the velocity duly proportioned to that of the Moon's shadow over the Earth as the Earth turns round its axis.

ON THE SUNNY SIDE OF THE STREET

Halley stationed observers within the path of totality in 1715 because he wished to check his calculations against the real eclipse. Several times in history, ambitious astronomers have tried the same experiment to improve their predictions, using feedback from observers. This was a way to evaluate methods of prediction and determine how accurate they were. Johannes Kepler had tried this as early as 1605. The solar eclipse of that year was not total in Prague, where Kepler was Imperial Mathematician at the court of the Holy Roman Emperor Rudolph II. But he had written to astronomers all over southern Europe asking them to send him reports on their position and their observations.

The year 1925 saw the most systematic attempt to use observers to check the exact outline of an eclipse path. A group of US astronomers arranged for observers to be stationed along the streets of Manhattan, with clear instructions to report what they saw. The southern edge of the Moon's shadow would pass over this populous area, providing an excellent opportunity to use many observers to determine the exact edge of the shadow.

From calculations based on lunar tables, the edge of the umbra was expected to cut across Manhattan, somewhere between 83rd Street and 110th Street. The total uncertainty of this prediction was approximately a mile (1.5 km). To check their predictions, the astronomers stationed observers at each intersection all the way from 72nd Street to 135th Street, usually on the tops of apartment blocks, so that they had the best possible view. Sixty-nine men were employed, and each was furnished with a piece of darkened glass. They were instructed to look at the Sun at the time of totality in order to see whether the corona was visible or whether a thin edge of the Sun was left shining. They were all instructed to report to a central office immediately after the eclipse.

Only one of the total of sixty-nine men wasn't sure whether he saw the corona, and the other sixty-eight all gave a clear-cut verdict. Riverside Drive runs north–south along the Hudson River. One observer, at 240 Riverside Drive, had seen the corona, a total eclipse, while a man located at 130 Riverside Drive had seen a small sliver of the Sun exposed, indicating that he had seen a partial eclipse. The distance between these two men was only about 225 feet (just under 70 m), about three times the width of 86th Street. This, then, was the accuracy to which the position of the edge of the shadow of totality was located on the east side of Manhattan Island (Figure 5.4).

Other observers along the East River were successful in making similar observations, with the result that the Moon's path across New York City was accurately determined. It is indeed surprising that such unanimity of opinion should be found among untrained observers who were all witnessing their first eclipse. Apparently it must be very easy to make up one's mind as to whether the corona is visible. Similar attempts had been made at previous eclipses, but had always met with failure. However, none of the Manhattan observers in 1925 saw the edge of the Moon's

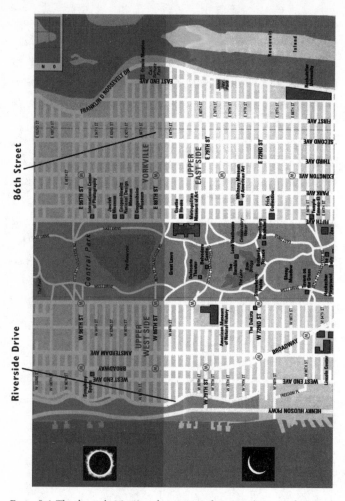

Figure 5.4. The edge of the Moon's umbra as it passed over Manhattan, as determined by rooftop observers at the total eclipse of 25 January 1925.

Baja, Mexico

Coast of South America

Figure 5.5. Composite photograph of the path of the Moon's shadow across the globe at the total eclipse of 11 July 1991, taken from a geosynchronous Earth satellite.

shadow on the ground, in spite of the excellent opportunity – the ground was completely covered with snow. Evidently, the edge of the Moon's shadow projected from the distance of the Moon's orbit is not sharply defined, but tapers off gradually.

This fuzzy edge of the Moon's shadow can be seen directly in the remarkable photograph shown in Figure 5.5. This was taken on 11 July 1991 from a satellite orbiting the Earth. This is a composite of images taken 30 minutes apart during the progress of that day's eclipse, which was viewed by the author from Baja Mexico, as described in the Prologue. The photograph was transmitted to receiving stations and placed on the Internet on the day of the eclipse. The shadow spot, about 300 km in diameter, moved from Hawaii to Mexico, then across Central and South America. An outline of the coast of South America is shown in the photograph.

Clearly, the path of totality is very narrow, and often, as in this instance, traverses oceans and remote areas of the globe. On 11 July 1991 many observers saw a partial eclipse from within the vast penumbra, which embraced most of North and South America. Coverage of the eclipse in the form of a complete map of the umbra and penumbra was published in a report by the US Naval Observatory 18 months beforehand, as for all modern eclipses. The map, shown in Figure 5.6, indicates the central path and the regions of visibility of the total eclipse and the partial eclipse from different parts of the globe. The exact path of totality first touched mainland North America at the Baja Peninsula after crossing the Pacific Ocean from Hawaii. In addition to maps of the eclipse path, the USNO publishes the exact timings, the precise locations of the Sun and the Moon on the celestial sphere, sky charts showing what stars and planets would be visible from different locations, and even the probable weather conditions.

This eclipse computing work has now been taken over by the NASA Space Flight Center in Greenbelt, Maryland. Fred Espenak of NASA publishes maps and data in advance of each

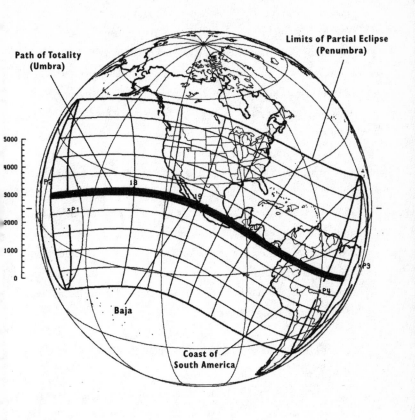

Figure 5.6. Computed path of the Moon's umbra and penumbra at the total eclipse of
11 July 1991.

eclipse, not only in booklet form but also on the Internet. The analytic techniques used for these predictions were developed by Friedrich Wilhelm Bessel, the nineteenth-century German mathematician. The mathematical devices known as Bessel functions allow celestial coordinates to be transformed into terrestrial coordinates. The reports give the precise latitude and longitude for points on the Earth in the path of totality listed at 5-minute intervals over the whole range of the eclipse. In addition, the exact coordinates of the Sun and the Moon on the celestial sphere are given for the exact time at the locations from which the eclipse will be visible. Finally, there are tables giving the precise times and local coordinates of first, second, third and fourth contact and maximum eclipse for hundreds of cities touched by the eclipse. Eclipse maps can be generated from these data by plotting the coordinates. This is a complete compendium of the eclipse. The NASA eclipse website contains a mass of interesting information.

WHERE ON EARTH IS THE MOON'S SHADOW?

The calculation of the exact location of the Moon's shadow may seem quite a technological feat. Indeed, the prediction of eclipse paths is a difficult process. Several independent factors affect the path at the same time. It is possible to get a feeling for the interplay of these factors by considering where the shadow falls on the Earth's surface in relation to the motion of the

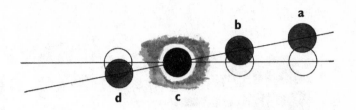

Figure 5.7. Eclipsing new Moons at different positions near a descending node.

Moon in its orbit near one of the nodes. Figure 5.7, which shows the Moon near a descending node, is similar to the diagrams in earlier chapters used to illustrate the ecliptic limits. The four positions a, b, c and d show eclipsing new Moons at four different positions with respect to a descending node. At position a, an eclipse occurs when the new Moon is some distance from the node and north of the ecliptic. This new Moon is within the ecliptic limit, so there is a partial eclipse. This position corresponds to position a in Figure 5.8. which shows the Moon and its projected shadow near the Earth.

When the new Moon is north of the ecliptic, the Moon's shadow is directed towards the northern hemisphere. A partial eclipse can be seen with the penumbra just covering the upper part of the northern hemisphere. In position b, the Moon has moved closer to the node though still north of the ecliptic. The eclipse is now close enough to the node to produce a total eclipse as shown in the corresponding diagram. Figure 5.8 b

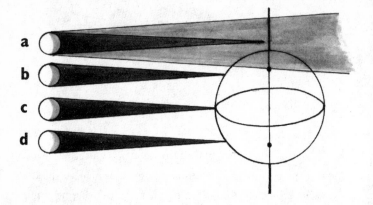

Figure 5.8. Projected shadows of eclipsing Moons for the corresponding positions in Figure 5.7.

shows that the umbra of the Moon's shadow now touches the Earth midway down the northern hemisphere.

At position c, the new Moon is on the ecliptic and the shadow falls very near the equator. In this case, a central eclipse, total or annular, takes place in or near the Tropics. Finally in position d, the eclipsing new Moon is south of the ecliptic and its shadow strikes the Earth in the southern hemisphere. Very roughly, this explains why an eclipse occurs at different latitude points on the globe, relating the view of the new Moon near a node and its shadow on the Earth.

These are only qualitative descriptions of the paths of solar eclipses. The accurate paths shown in charts like Figure 5.6 have been calculated by computer using techniques which simultaneously include the influence of all the variables in a more exact way.

TOTALITY: HOW LONG?

The duration of the eclipse at a particular location on the globe is all important for eclipse-chasers around the world. At a given location it depends chiefly on three variables: the orbital speed of the Moon as it passes the Sun; the rotational speed of the Earth at that location and the size of the shadow. The size of the shadow depends on the orbital distances of the Moon from the Earth and of the Earth from the Sun. Also, the degree of elongation of the shadow caused by the Earth's curvature is a factor. This is determined by the time of the day at which the shadow falls at a particular location.

Once the diameter of the shadow as intercepted by the Earth is known, it is easy to find the duration of totality. First, the speed of the shadow across the Earth must be calculated. The Moon advances in its orbit approximately one diameter in an hour, or more exactly, at about 3,400 km/h (on average, depending on its distance from the Earth). This is almost the same speed at which the Moon's shadow passes across the Earth. However, because of the rotation of the Earth on its axis, an observer on the Earth will be moving with the shadow, effectively slowing it down.

As the shadow speeds along the Earth's surface, the Earth rotates in the same direction, as do observers on the Earth, essentially slowing down the shadow. This is like two cars on a motorway. If an observer is travelling at, say, 100 km/h and a second car approaches from behind at 150 km/h, the observer in the first car will see the faster car overtaking at a relative speed of 50 km/h. We can think of 100 km/h as the 'slowing speed'. During the eclipse of 30 June 1973, the supersonic jet Concorde increased this 'slowing speed' by flying within the umbra in the same direction as the shadow. Observers in the aircraft were able to view the total eclipse for 74 minutes, about ten times longer than the theoretical maximum for a stationary observer on the Earth.

An observer at the Earth's equator will complete a 24-hour rotation at a speed of 1,670 km/h. This is the maximum 'slowing speed': at higher northern or southern latitudes an observer's circle of latitude has a smaller circumference because of the curvature of the Earth, and the slowing speed is lower the nearer an observer is to one of the poles. The Moon moves in its orbit from west to east, so its shadow traverses the Earth in the same direction as the Earth rotates. This is the direction in which an observer is carried by the Earth's rotation, so the Moon's shadow path travels with respect to the Earth's surface at a rate which is the difference between the two speeds. At the equator, the speed of the shadow is reduced the most: it travels at $3,372 - 1,670 = 1,702$ km/h. This is as slow as the Moon's shadow can ever move. Consequently, the longest eclipses occur near the equator where the slowing speed of the Earth's rotation is a maximum. For a shadow diameter of 200 km and a net speed of 1,702 km/h, the duration of the eclipse is just over 7 minutes. The absolute theoretical maximum is 7 minutes and 31 seconds, which occurs when the Moon is at perigee and its shadow diameter on the Earth is a maximum.

If Edmond Halley were alive today, he would be an eclipse-chaser *par excellence*. Using modern technological devices from mountain-top observatories to Earth satellites, the Astronomer Royal of three hundred years ago would no doubt be photographing, timing, measuring and analysing all aspects of this most exacting conjunction of the Sun and Moon.

THE SUN'S SURFACE: VICTORIAN SOLAR ECLIPSES

Never by any means will we be able to study
the chemical composition of the stars.

Auguste Comte

I N HIS *COURS DE PHILOSOPHIE POSITIVE*, published in the 1830s, the French philosopher and sociologist Auguste Comte (1798–1857) expressed, in the words above, his pessimism about the future of astronomy, particularly with respect to the stars. This he used as an example of the limitations of science in explaining the whole universe. Though he believed that only natural phenomena verified by experiments could explain the world, Comte recognised our limited ability to obtain empirical verification. He gave the make-up of the stars as an example of knowledge forever beyond human reach.

Few would have argued with him then. Yet technological developments would make such predictions about science foolhardy. Before the nineteenth century was over, more was known about the composition of the Sun and other stars than was known about our close satellite, the non-luminous Moon. Not until its exploration by astronauts in the late twentieth century has the make-up of the Moon been confirmed. This unexpected knowledge of the stars was a result of a collaboration between physicists and astronomers investigating solar eclipses which lasted right through the nineteenth century.

It was in 1664, in England, that the understanding of the composition of light really began. Isaac Newton (1642–1727) discovered that white light, which might be thought, intuitively, to have no colour, in fact contains all the colours the eye can see. Simply by passing a light beam through a glass prism, Newton demonstrated how a spectrum is formed, the light spreading out into the colours of the rainbow. This phenomenon of the spreading of light into its constituent colours is called dispersion.

But it was not until a century and a half later that this spectrum of dispersed light was analysed in the laboratory. In 1814, the German physicist Joseph von Fraunhofer (1787–1826) placed a narrow slit in front of a prism and viewed the spectrum of light passing through this combination with a small telescope eyepiece. By this technique he was able to investigate the spectrum bit by bit, colour by colour. Different colours of light are produced by waves of different sizes whose lengths can be measured, and thus a number could be associated with each colour.

Figure 6.1. The spectrum of colours formed by passing sunlight through a glass prism. Based on a drawing made by Isaac Newton in 1672.

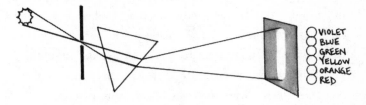

As light waves have very short wavelengths, it was decided to introduce a new unit of length, later named the angstrom (symbol Å) after the Swedish astronomer Anders Ångström. One hundred million angstroms equal one centimetre.

The range of wavelengths corresponding to the coloured spectrum of light, known as the visible spectrum, could then be expressed in convenient numbers, and turned out to have values between about 4000 Å and 7000 Å. Violet fell at the short-wavelength end, at about 4000 Å, while red fell at the long-wavelength end, at about 7000 Å. The light beyond these end points, the ultraviolet past the short end and the infrared past the long end, cannot be seen by the human eye. But in between these values were all the colours that can be seen. Fraunhofer was able to calibrate his new combination of prism, slit and eyepiece so that he could precisely measure all the wavelengths in the visible spectrum.

Like most discoveries in science, it seems that serendipity played its part when Fraunhofer decided to examine a beam of sunlight with his apparatus. He had expected the Sun to exhibit a continuous spectrum of colours, as it is essentially a luminous body emitting white light. But in addition to the continuous coloured spectrum, he saw something surprising. As he reported in his journal, he saw 'an almost countless number of strong or weak vertical lines which are darker than the rest of the coloured image; some appeared to be almost perfectly black'. Though Fraunhofer was surprised at the appearance of these lines, he knew they were real. 'I have convinced myself by

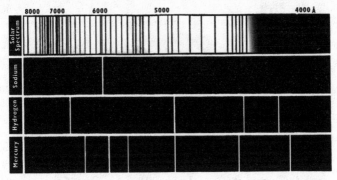

Figure 6.2. Fraunhofer lines in the solar spectrum (top) and bright line spectra of sodium, hydrogen and mercury.

numerous experiments and by various methods that these lines and bands are due to the nature of sunlight and do not arise from diffraction or optical illusions, etc.' Fraunhofer was the first to observe and measure the wavelengths of the dark lines. It seems natural enough that these 'gaps' in the solar spectrum became known as Fraunhofer lines.

But why should there be dark lines in the middle of the Sun's spectrum? This was a puzzling phenomenon. In his laboratory Fraunhofer had already studied pure chemical elements like heated mercury vapour and nitrogen gas, using the same set-up of prism, slit and eyepiece. For elements he observed sequences of bright coloured lines on a dark background. These sharply defined and easily recognisable patterns were called line spectra. No two gases were seen to have the same set of bright lines. It soon became clear that line spectra were characteristic

147

of a particular element and could be used to identify the presence of that element in the substance emitting the light. This was like a signature of the element written in the distinct pattern of bright coloured lines. The Fraunhofer lines and the bright line spectra of a few elements are shown in Figure 6.2.

Shortly after these developments, similar but more fundamental work was taken up in the university town of Heidelberg. The German physicist Gustav Kirchhoff (1824–87) was working with Robert Bunsen (1811–99), the man who made the famous burner with the colourless flame. They had combined the prism, telescopic eyepiece and slit into a single instrument which had become known as a spectroscope. With this and the famous burner, they were able to analyse many different elements and confirm that each had its own characteristic pattern of bright coloured lines.

One evening, the story goes, the two men were looking out of their laboratory window in Heidelberg at a fire raging in the nearby town of Mannheim. Curious about what might be burning, they pointed their spectroscope at the flames. They were able to detect the presence of the elements barium and strontium in the fire, whose spectra they had previously identified in their laboratory. The question struck them immediately: if they could analyse flames in Mannheim, why not the surface of the Sun?

Kirchhoff thought of Fraunhofer's dark lines in the solar spectrum and began to study them using an ingenious method.

First he made a solution containing sodium. A sodium flame, when seen through a spectroscope, was known to have a pair of bright yellow lines which could easily be identified. By superimposing these bright yellow lines onto the Fraunhofer solar spectrum by a clever method of projection, Kirchhoff found an exact match with a pair of the Sun's dark lines. This suggested to him that the Fraunhofer lines might be due to the presence of sodium vapour in the outer atmosphere of the Sun.

This seemed to make sense. Kirchhoff knew that when a gaseous element is extremely hot, it emits bright lines at specific wavelengths. This emission spectrum is characteristic of the gas and acts as a signature of the element. From this he hypothesised that if the same gas is cool, it will absorb light at the same distinct wavelength. In short, the cool gas is absorbing light at its characteristic wavelengths, giving what is called an absorption spectrum of dark lines. These lines are at the same wavelengths as the bright lines in the spectrum of light which the gas emits when it is hot. The absorption spectrum is the negative of the emission spectrum. This meant that the presence of an element could be established by its emission or absorption spectrum.

The results of Kirchhoff's laboratory experiments allowed him to formulate three rules governing the emission and absorption of radiation by solids, liquids and gases. The first rule states that when a solid or liquid is heated, it emits light with a continuous spectrum: without any distinct bright lines. The second law states that if a gas or vapour composed of a single element is heated, it will emit light whose spectrum consists of bright lines at definite wavelengths. The third law states that the same gas when cool will absorb light at the wavelengths at which it emits light when hot – that is, it reverses its characteristic spectrum from bright lines to dark lines.

Applying these laws to the Sun, Kirchhoff assumed that the visible surface of the Sun, called the photosphere, consisted of a hot liquid. The photosphere should therefore emit a continuous spectrum. He also assumed that a cooler gaseous layer overlays the photosphere. According to Kirchhoff's third law, this layer should absorb from the photosphere light at the wavelengths of its characteristic spectral lines. This absorption causes the dark lines in the spectrum, the Fraunhofer lines, which thus appear in silhouette against the continuous spectrum of the photosphere. This gave Kirchhoff a complete explanation for his experiment of superimposing the spectrum of sodium onto the spectrum of the Sun. This proved conclusively that sodium is in the Sun's atmosphere.

Thus, by studying the dark lines in the spectrum of the Sun or even of a distant star, it seemed that one could deduce what elements were present in its outer atmosphere. If Auguste Comte could have followed the lines of this research, thirty-five years after making his remark about knowledge outside the reach of humankind, he might have begun to feel that he had been somewhat rash.

ECLIPSES OF THE SUN: THE SOLAR CORONA AND PROMINENCES

The explanation that Kirchhoff had given of the dark absorption lines in the solar spectrum presupposed the existence of an atmosphere of hot gases surrounding the Sun. However, at the time empirical knowledge of the physics of the Sun's surface was sketchy. But one of those strange coincidences in history was about to take place. Astronomers in the second half of the nineteenth century were just becoming interested in the Sun's surface for other reasons, namely to explain observations made during total eclipses of the Sun.

While chemists and physicists like Fraunhofer and Kirchhoff were making progress with new models and diagnostic tools, astronomers from all over the world were planning to observe the totally eclipsed Sun in 1842 and in 1851. Their focus would be to interpret the nature of the Sun's corona and the spectacular prominences, large luminous clouds that extended outwards from the Sun's surface, both phenomena seen only during a total eclipse.

The astronomer who did most to stimulate interest in these prominences was Francis Baily (1774–1844). Baily had made a fortune as a stockbroker, and after his retirement in 1825 dedicated himself to astronomy (he had helped to found the Royal Astronomical Society during the 1820s). Though he was mainly interested in cataloguing stars, he was keen to journey to Scotland

Figure 6.3. Baily's beads: the breaking up of light at the edge of the Moon just before second contact. The effect is due to the last rays of sunlight streaming between mountains on the Moon.

in 1836 to witness an annular eclipse, which he had heard produces spectacular effects. In his report of the eclipse to the Royal Astronomical Society he described for the first time an effect which, although he was not the first to discover it, has since been named after him – Baily's beads. In his own words, 'A row of lucid points, like a string of beads, irregular in size and distant from each other, suddenly formed round that part of the circumference of the Moon that was about to enter onto the Sun's disc.'

In his reports, Baily urged his fellow astronomers to pay particular heed to other phenomena around the Sun's edge when they observed future eclipses. He was referring to the ghostly corona, the spectacular prominences and the lucid beads of light. Baily wanted to settle the controversy then current as to whether these phenomena were solar or lunar in origin. In the case of the beads it turned out to be both: they are caused by the last beams of light from the eclipsed Sun streaming between mountains at the edge of the Moon's disk.

Six years later, Baily travelled to Italy for the total eclipse of 8 July 1842. This time he was astounded by the size and brilliance of the corona and the presence of four large, rose-coloured prominences that extended well away from the eclipsed Sun. Baily's report and those of others for the 1842 eclipse generated much interest among European astronomers about the nature of these effects.

It was at this 1842 eclipse that a new era began, with the application of photography to astronomy. It had been only three years since the Frenchman Louis Daguerre had caused a sensation by producing a photographic image on a copper plate. This process generally needed long exposures of 20–30 minutes, and was therefore not very not successful for portraiture – no model could sit still for that long. But the partially eclipsed Sun of 1842 was bright enough to produce an image, the first eclipse photograph in history. The following year, a daguerreotype image was obtained of the spectrum of the Sun (in black and white, of course). In July 1851 the big breakthrough came with the first photograph of a total eclipse of the Sun. Taken in Germany, the photo was rushed to London and displayed at the

Great Exhibition of 1851. By this time solar eclipses had become a topic of conversation in the smart salons and coffee houses of London and cities on the Continent.

The 1851 eclipse skirted the Baltic seaboard and crossed into Scandinavia. Over a hundred astronomers from Britain, Scandinavia and Germany were positioned within the path of totality, and most enjoyed clear skies. After comparing many of the observational accounts, the Royal Astronomical Society issued an unambiguous report expressing its satisfaction that the corona was associated with the Sun. Likewise, the red prominences revealed on the eastern and western limbs of the Sun by the advancing Moon most decisively proved that these wonderful phenomena belonged to the Sun and not the Moon.

The second half of the century brought even more revelations about eclipses. The central line of a solar eclipse passed directly over London in 1858, but it was annular and of no interest to astronomers studying the corona and prominences, for these effects can be seen only during a total eclipse – or so it was thought at the time. Solar eclipses would also be visible from North America and Spain in 1860, and from India in 1868. By this time travel was becoming easier and cheaper, and it became accepted for astronomers to set up temporary observatories along the line of the eclipse path. These stations were equipped with increasingly elaborate instruments to study in scientific detail what had previously been regarded as only an interesting or portentous spectacle.

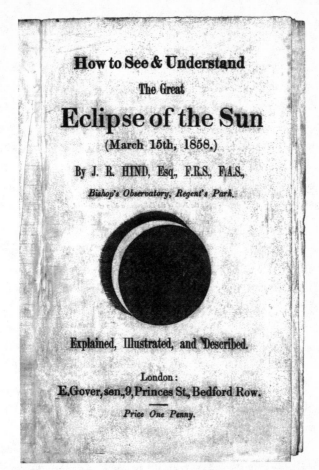

How to See & Understand

The Great

Eclipse of the Sun

(March 15th, 1858.)

By J. R. HIND, Esq., F.R.S., F.A.S.,

Bishop's Observatory, Regent's Park.

Explained, Illustrated, and Described.

London:
E. Gover, sen., 9, Princes St., Bedford Row.

Price One Penny.

Figure 6.4. The central path of a solar eclipse which passed directly over London in 1858. However, it was an annular eclipse and thus of little interest to the Victorian astronomers studying the corona and the prominences, which are visible only at a total eclipse of the Sun.

Following on from the pioneering work of Daguerre, the eclipse of 1860 was noteworthy mainly for the wide application of photography to the observation of solar eclipses. In place of drawings hastily sketched during the few minutes of totality, or written reports based on memory, photographic images would from now on dominate eclipse reports. Three different groups got excellent photos of the Sun's prominences, and all agreed that these were part of the Sun's atmosphere. That matter, at least, was settled once and for all. The ability to transport and use photographic apparatus to record images of the corona and prominences was clearly demonstrated for future expeditions.

SPECTROSCOPY AND THE SOLAR ECLIPSE

A breakthrough was imminent. Physicists and astronomers were working together to study the surface of the Sun. The crucial spectroscopic experiments performed by Kirchhoff on the Fraunhofer lines were well understood. Photography was now a standard experimental technique of eclipse observations. The composition of the Sun's atmosphere, corona and prominences could now be recorded and analysed by these techniques. The science of eclipses had reached a new plateau.

Researchers now asked what spectrum the prominences would give when examined with a spectroscope. What were they made of? Apparently they were not masses of dense material shot up to great heights by some explosive action on the Sun. Even before the advent of photography it could be seen that the laws of gravitation

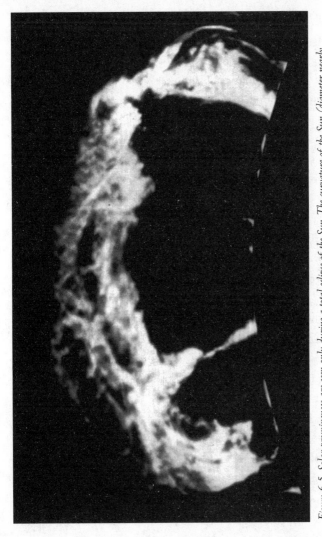

Figure 6.5. Solar prominences are seen only during a total eclipse of the Sun. The curvature of the Sun (diameter nearly 1,400,000 km) indicates the enormous size of these gaseous formations.

would not allow such material to hang above the Sun, even for the short periods of a total eclipse. Theories proliferated.

A distinct difference in colour had been noted between the red flames of the prominences and the white body of the Sun. Many believed that the prominences probably consisted of only a few gases, with hydrogen, the lightest known element, one of the chief constituents. The visible spectrum of hydrogen was known from laboratory emission experiments. It consisted of a bright line in the red, and another one in the blue, followed by a series of other lines getting closer together as they approached the violet end of the spectrum. Astronomers guessed that the strong red line could easily be responsible for the red colour of the prominences.

If the prominences were actually eruptions of hydrogen gas heated to great temperatures in the solar furnace, their spectrum should be vastly different from the ordinary solar spectrum. Furthermore, if the prominences were gaseous their spectrum should consist of bright emission lines against a dark background, with none of the dark Fraunhofer lines characteristic of light from the Sun's surface. There was only one way to find out: apply the techniques of Fraunhofer and Kirchhoff, and look directly at the prominences with a spectroscope.

INDIA: THE SOLAR ECLIPSE OF 1868

It was with much enthusiasm and heightened expectations that European astronomers travelled to far-off India for the solar eclipse of 18 August 1868. The eclipse attracted large expeditions from all over Europe, two from Britain, two French, one German and one Spanish. This was to be the first time the new technique of spectroscopy would be applied to the eclipsed Sun. The scene was set for a watershed investigation in which physics, chemistry and astronomy would join forces, hopefully to explain the nature of solar prominences.

Several observers saw bright emission lines in the spectrum of the prominences, as had been anticipated. But the surprises started with the French astronomer Jules Janssen (1824–1907). Like the others, Janssen was attempting to study the spectrum of solar prominences during the eclipse. He recorded the appearance of half a dozen bright emission lines which coincided exactly with the lines already identified with hydrogen. Naturally, he concluded that the prominences must be composed of hot hydrogen gas. Janssen, however, also noted a bright yellow emission line which was usually identified with sodium. Yet he determined that this bright line was at a slightly shorter wavelength than the known sodium line. Puzzled, he asked himself why comparatively heavy sodium vapour should be floating around in the solar prominences.

Then an idea struck Janssen which changed things completely. Impressed with how bright the prominences appeared during the eclipse, he wondered whether these lines could be seen with his spectroscope under normal circumstances, without having to wait for the darkness of an eclipse. He knew that an increase in the dispersion – more spreading of the light – would diminish the brightness of the background of the solar spectrum. Since the continuous spectrum contains many wavelengths, an increase in dispersion would reduce the brightness by spreading out those wavelengths. Fewer waves would get into the spectroscope. However, a bright emission line exists at a single wavelength, and its brightness would not be affected by the increased dispersion. Consequently, Janssen reasoned, the prominences might be visible in normal daylight through the spectroscope since the emission lines would be detectable through the weakened atmospheric glare.

The arrival of clouds immediately after the Indian eclipse on 18 August kept Janssen from experimenting until the next day. Then, in broad daylight, he focused the slit of his spectroscope just outside the edge of the Sun. To his great surprise and delight he saw the bright hydrogen emission lines and the strange 'sodium' line, at the same position where a prominence had appeared the day before. He could now examine these lines at his leisure. Remaining in India for the next three weeks, he monitored the spectra of the prominences and prepared a report on his findings to be sent to the French Academy.

A NEW ELEMENT ON THE SUN

One of the most important eclipse astronomers of the day was missing from the group that had travelled to view the Indian eclipse of 1868. This was the English astronomer Norman Lockyer (1836–1920). Lockyer was born the year before Queen

Figure 6.6. Sir Norman Lockyer.

Victoria came to the throne. The son of a surgeon and apothecary, the young man did not follow his father's profession but turned to the arts, becoming fluent in French, German and Greek. After a stint as a language teacher he obtained a post as a temporary clerk in the War Office. Lockyer developed an interest in astronomy. He met Thomas Cooke the telescope-maker, and in 1861 purchased from him a 3.75-inch (95 mm) instrument of his own. He began a serious study of the heavens. Now a determined and ambitious country gentleman, he taught himself the technical aspects of astronomical research, and purchased several excellent telescopes with which to pursue his studies. In the 1860s, he too became interested in spectroscopy and investigations of the Sun during solar eclipses.

In January 1862 he made the following entry in his notebook:

Having now by the grace of God obtained the means, I hope and believe, of doing good work in astronomy. It becomes necessary to start a book in which to record any observations, such at least I consider worthy of record, on paper. For besides that which is best jotted down by the pen there will be an infinity to be treasured up by the mind. This too may be put on record some day.

This example of florid Victorian prose marked the start of a career that would change not only astronomy, but Britain's attitude towards science.

It very quickly became clear that Lockyer's work was of the highest quality, and he received a grant from the Royal Society in 1866 to fund the construction of a powerful spectroscope which he designed himself. With this instrument he would be capable of capturing the light of a solar prominence. He designed a special spectroscope–telescope, but its fabrication took over two years. The instrument was not ready by August 1868 when the European astronomers sailed for India, which is why he missed the eclipse.

Lockyer was just as interested in the study of the corona and the prominences as was Janssen, but he was one step ahead of

Figure 6.7. Lockyer's special spectroscope, used to view the spectrum of the Sun without a solar eclipse.

the Frenchman. Lockyer had already guessed, independently of Janssen, that the prominences might be visible through a spectroscope at times other than at an eclipse. This is why he had taken the trouble to develop a spectroscope of special design. On 20 October 1868, when the new spectroscope finally arrived at Cambridge, he immediately trained it on the Sun in broad daylight. Straight away he had his suspicion confirmed – that the spectrum of the Sun's prominences could be seen without a solar eclipse, the same conclusion demonstrated by Janssen in India two months earlier.

Lockyer wrote at once to the French Academy of Science, and by an extraordinary coincidence his letter arrived within a few minutes of Janssen's. They were read one after the other at the same meeting of the Academy, on 26 October 1868. In a generous gesture, the French Academy honoured both astronomers for this discovery and in later years even minted a commemorative medal bearing their images side by side.

Immediately after his recognition by the French Academy, Lockyer made a new discovery. Examining the edge of the Sun with his new solar spectroscope, he noticed the same bright yellow line in the spectrum that Janssen had seen. But Lockyer would not accept that it was sodium. Perhaps the resolution of his instrument was more precise than those used by Janssen and others. Only a month later, he established that the mysterious yellow prominence line differed in wavelength from that of sodium. He put the unknown orange-yellow line at 5876 Å, some distance from the sodium line at 5893 Å. But if it was not sodium, what was it?

Neither Lockyer nor Janssen could reproduce the spectral features of the line in the laboratory. By 1870, after many failures, Lockyer was convinced that he had discovered a new chemical element, one present only in the Sun and not on the Earth. He called it 'helium', from the Greek word *helios* for 'Sun'. Lockyer was widely criticised by other astronomers who thought him far too hasty. Understandably, they were reluctant to accept the existence of a new element on the basis of a single spectral line. Nevertheless, Lockyer persisted in his belief that a new gas, never detected on the Earth, was present at the surface of the Sun.

For the next quarter of a century after Lockyer's 'discovery', helium remained a mysterious hypothetical gas known only from the bright yellow line in the spectrum of the solar prominences. In 1895 the Scottish chemist William Ramsay (1852–1916) secured a sample of cleveite, a variety of radioactive uraninite, which he purified and sealed in a discharge tube. Looking through the tube with a small hand spectroscope, he was startled to see an intense yellow ray, with a few fainter ones in the red and green. A quick check showed that the yellow ray was not coincident with the sodium line. The wavelength was measured and found to be 5876 Å – the same value that Lockyer had measured. Ramsay sent samples of the gas to both Lockyer and William Crookes, a physicist famous for experimenting on cathode rays. Crookes confirmed that the gas was the same as the one Lockyer had observed near the surface of the Sun. When he heard the news, Lockyer was beside himself with joy as he squinted through the spectroscope at the 'glorious yellow effulgence' he had first detected on the Sun a quarter of a century before.

Thus, only a few decades after Comte had confidently predicted that the composition of the stars would never be known, a new element had been discovered on our closest star, the Sun, and an uneclipsed Sun at that. This was the beginning of a new era in astronomy in which spectroscopic analysis would be used to determine the composition, the speed and even the age of stars.

An interesting footnote to the work of Janssen and Lockyer is provided by their expedition to the island of Sicily for the solar eclipse of 1870, from which we can get an impression of what it was like to be an eclipse astronomer in the Victorian era. Janssen, though lame from a childhood accident, travelled extensively on eclipse expeditions. He was scheduled to meet Lockyer in Sicily to continue their work on the eclipsed Sun. This was the time of the Franco-Prussian War, and the Prussian armies were laying siege to Paris. In spite of the siege, Janssen would not be deterred from travelling. When the time came, he escaped from the French capital in a hot-air balloon.

Lockyer had his own problems in getting to Sicily. He had obtained a grant from the Treasury and the use of two gunboats from the War Office to transport his eclipse equipment to Sicily. The two parties were to rendezvous in Naples, where Janssen was to join them. While the Frenchman was leaving Paris by balloon, one of Lockyer's gunboats ran aground in the Bay of Naples. But somehow these hardships were overcome, and the expedition reached its destination in Sicily. As they prepared for the big day, the two men must have been proud of themselves to have finally arrived in spite of such formidable adversity. At the appointed hour, they watched in frustration as clouds gathered to block the eclipse – and nothing was seen.

Undaunted upon returning to England, Lockyer set about organising another expedition to India for the eclipse of the following year. This expedition was funded by the British Association, and once more Lockyer arranged for the use of two gunboats. When the astronomical instruments reached India they were set up in the tower of a disused fort at Bekul. But the gun-like appearance of the telescopes and some target practice by the gunboat crews convinced the local population that war had been declared. They were ready to flee to the hills when it was explained to them that they were in no danger.

But that was not the end of the trouble. On 12 December 1871, as Lockyer and his colleagues waited anxiously for totality under brilliant clear skies, smoke began to appear from everywhere. The Indians did not like the sight of the disappearing Sun and had begun to light fires all around the fort, preparing sacrifices to placate the gods. The astronomers panicked as the smoke began to obscure their view of the nearly eclipsed Sun, and called out the local police of the powerful British Raj to chase away the people and extinguish the fires.

In the end all was well. Lockyer managed to observe his first total eclipse of the Sun with his new spectroscope. No longer was the Sun a white-hot featureless ball of gas. He now knew the nature of the Sun's surface, its photosphere, and its Fraunhofer spectrum. Lockyer could also claim to have some

Figure 6.8. The Indian eclipse of December 1871. Norman Lockyer is seen resting under the umbrella.

understanding of the atmosphere surrounding the Sun, including the solar prominences and the corona, which for a long time had puzzled the eclipse astronomers.

Lockyer organised many eclipse expeditions over the next forty years, though 1870 marked the start of another important phase of his life in which he used the force of his powerful personality and his significant influence to improve science education and prepare Britain for the twentieth century. He permanently damaged one of his eyes while peering at the Sun, but this proved no hindrance to a distinguished scientific career which even touched on ancient astronomy. He was one of the first to propose that Stonehenge was a megalithic astronomical observatory. As a man of many interests, he wrote the first book on the St Andrews rules of golf, founded the Science Museum in South Kensington, London, and launched the still published international science journal *Nature*, which he edited for fifty years. Norman Lockyer belongs to a century of self-made men and expert amateurs who shaped the science of the century that was to follow, and deserves to be remembered with the best of them.

CONFIRMING GENERAL RELATIVITY

The Eclipse of 29 May 1919

Then I would have been sorry for the dear Lord.
The theory is correct.

Albert Einstein, 1919

O N 14 JUNE 1360 a cycle of 71 solar eclipses, now known as saros series 136, began when the Moon's penumbra barely touched the southern polar region. Modern computations of the paths of the other 70 eclipse tracks across the globe tell us that the last in this series will just graze the north polar region on 30 July 2622. Near the mid-point of this 1,262-year cycle, on 29 May 1919, the 32nd eclipse in the series cast its shadow across the tropics.

On that day the Moon's shadow touched the Earth just west of South America and moved across Peru, Bolivia and Brazil to the Atlantic Ocean. Continuing its journey over the southern part of Africa, the shadow finally disappeared at sunset in the Indian Ocean. Just before reaching the west coast of Africa, the shadow had traversed the small island of Principe. Waiting there, with a powerful telescope and a large-format camera, was the English astronomer Arthur Eddington, ready to photograph the stars behind the eclipsed Sun. Several thousand kilometres away in his Berlin study, the German physicist Albert Einstein patiently awaited the results.

EINSTEIN AND EDDINGTON

It is hard to imagine two scientists more different than Eddington and Einstein. Yet they were destined to collaborate in solving one of the greatest puzzles of the universe.

Einstein (1879–1955) was the son of a Swiss German businessman who worked hard to provide the best possible education for his offspring. But Albert loathed Switzerland's rigid system of schooling. He attended a Catholic elementary school and then a Gymnasium (high school). He was no model pupil, arguing with his teachers and showing little respect for them or their teaching. He completed his undergraduate degree at the Technische Hochschule (Technical High School) in Zurich, helped through his examination by his well-organised friend Marcel Grossman. Einstein day-dreamed and read the latest publications in physics journals while Grossman took careful notes. Einstein said of this period that cramming for his examinations had such a deterring effect on him that for an entire year afterwards he found it distasteful to consider any scientific problem. The year after receiving his degree, he applied everywhere for a job. As a problem student, the young and disappointed scientist found he could not obtain an academic position.

Finally, on 23 June 1902, Einstein started work at the Swiss Patent Office in Berne as probationary Technical Expert, Third Class, on the modest salary of 3,500 francs per year. He quickly became adept at the work, and was happy to be free of the hostile academic world that had brought him repeated heartache. In his spare time he could work quietly and with growing excitement on developing his revolutionary ideas. In this unlikely conservatory, his genius matured.

In 1905, at the age of twenty-six, Einstein was already contributing papers to scientific journals. That year he had four papers published in the *Annalen der Physik*, the prestigious German physics journal. The third paper, the most interesting to Einstein, was entitled 'On the electrodynamics of moving bodies', a subject that has since become known as the special theory of relativity. In this paper Einstein solved most of the problems that still remained in classical physics, but to do so he had to change for ever the way we think of time and space. He drastically modified the underlying assumptions of the Newtonian universe.

Einstein had his own way of investigating the puzzles he found in the physical universe. He would ask himself 'What if …' type questions. The hypothetical situations he imagined could never be realised in practice but were consistent with the laws of physics. He called these *gedanken* or 'thought' experiments, carried out in a kind of laboratory of the mind. For the special theory of relativity of 1905, he asked how two different observers would experience or record a sudden bolt of lightning in the sky. One observer he imagined to be in a moving train, while the second observer was at rest on a platform as the moving train passed by.

the moon   the earth

SUNLIGHT REACHES THE MOON *(see page 1)*

Part of the Sun is drawn to scale on the inside front cover of this book. The separation between the Moon and Earth would be 54.6 mm. The Earth and the Moon and their separation are shown to scale. The Earth's diameter is 1.83 mm to scale, and the Moon's diameter is 0.5 mm. Why page 175? Because we need nearly the entire extent of this book, from the inside front cover to page 175, to represent on this scale the distance from the Sun to the Earth. This is with all the pages opened out like an accordion, double-sided. At this distance the image of the Sun viewed from the Earth shrinks to 0.5 mm, and is just small enough to be obstructed by the image of the Moon, which is also 0.5 mm across on this scale.

Applying strict logic and consistency in this thought experiment, Einstein insisted that there should be symmetry in the laws of physics for both observers. He believed that with uniform motion it should not matter which observer is considered to be at rest and which is considered to be moving. The laws of physics as experienced by the two observers had to be equivalent. For example, it makes no difference if the observer on the platform is imagined to be moving towards a stationary train, rather than the observer in the moving train moving towards the observer on the platform: the results of any measurement should be the same. Einstein's only postulate was that the speed of light was a constant, that both observers would measure light to be travelling at the same speed, regardless of which of them is considered to be moving and which is at rest.

Einstein found that if he accepted these arguments he would have to abandon the concept of absolute time, thought of as a clock ticking away somewhere at the centre of the universe. He would also have to dispose of the concept of absolute space, a grid of fixed coordinates spread out through the universe. He concluded that his two observers would see each other's clocks ticking at different rates, and find each other's measuring rules to be of different lengths. A characteristic time for each of the two observers, the moving and the stationary, needed to be added to the usual three space dimensions to completely specify the condition (the 'state') of a system. This became known as the fourth dimension. These ideas opened up a fissure in the framework of Newtonian physics which could be repaired only by redefining the nature of space and time.

Arthur Eddington (1882–1944), born into a devout Quaker family at Kendal in the foothills of England's beautiful Lake District, was three years younger than Einstein. As a dutiful son of a successful schoolmaster, he was a model student, almost the antithesis of his German colleague. Yet he had the same obsessive fascination with the physical universe. With determination and careful guidance through all the hoop-jumping of the English educational system, Eddington made it to Cambridge at the age of twenty, entering Trinity College in the autumn of 1902. He finished the three-year Tripos course in mathematics and physics at Cambridge in just two years, and when the results were declared his name headed the list. Never before had a second-year man won such a distinction.

After lecturing for a year at Cambridge, Eddington was offered the post of Chief Assistant at the Royal Observatory in Greenwich, and his career as an astronomer began. He immediately contributed important work on contemporary problems in astronomy, particularly on the motion of stars and the structure of the universe. In 1914 he returned to Cambridge as Plumian Professor of Astronomy. By this time Eddington knew of Einstein's published work on special relativity, but was not aware of the German's struggle to generalise the conclusions of the 1905 paper to non-uniform motion.

THE PRINCIPLE OF EQUIVALENCE

Einstein had what one might call artistic objections to his own theory of special relativity. In this theory he had considered a train moving uniformly past a stationary observer. From this he was able to show that there is no difference between the observer in the moving train and the observer on the platform in terms of the measured observations. Now he asked what would happen if the train was accelerating. Why should uniform motion be special? How much more satisfying it would be if all motion, uniform or not, were relative. The laws of physics would then be the same in any frame of reference.

But the facts were clearly against him. The observer in an accelerating train will not experience his surroundings in the same way as a stationary observer. We all know this, and do not need to study Newton to be convinced of it. In a smoothly moving train we feel no sense of motion other than the vibration of the carriage. But if the train accelerates, it causes a lurch which we feel at once.

To bring gravity into the picture, imagine, instead of the train, a lift going to the top of a tall building. In a lift moving at uniform speed we detect no evidence of motion other than the vibration of the lifting gear. But at the start and finish of the journey we feel an odd sensation in the stomach caused by the acceleration and deceleration of the lift. Einstein decided to try another *gedanken* experiment to examine accelerated motion, when the speed is changing. This led to another kind of equivalence.

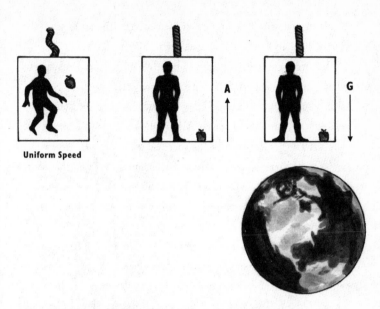

Uniform Speed

Figure 7.1. The principle of equivalence I: The acceleration A is equivalent to the gravitational pull G for a passenger in a windowless lift.

Imagine a passenger lift set adrift in space far from other gravitational bodies. Its occupants would feel no 'weight'. An apple 'dropped' by someone in the lift would not fall to the floor but would remain suspended at the point where it was released. This weightlessness is familiar from images of astronauts in a free-falling space capsule in orbit around the Earth. Now, imagine accelerating the lift in a direction that the occupants would call 'up' at a rate that increases its speed by 9.8 metres per second in each second. This is the magnitude of the acceleration caused by gravity as measured at the surface of the Earth. The floor will accelerate up and hit the apple.

We may ask at this point, 'The lift is accelerated relative to what?' Einstein stated in the special theory that it is not possible to measure the absolute speed of a single object, only its speed relative to something else. Although the speed cannot be detected, its acceleration or the increase of the speed, 9.8 metres per second every second, can be. For example, it gives the occupants of the lift the sensation of 'weight', for they are pushed to the floor. This change can be felt in the same way as the lurch in the accelerated train.

Now, if a planet exactly like the Earth is moved past the same lift with its occupants, they experience exactly the same sensation as they did in the upwardly accelerating lift in outer space. They feel weight, and the apple hits the floor. The passengers might wish to distinguish the upwardly accelerating lift from the pull of the moving planet, but they cannot. If there are no windows in the lift, there is no experiment they can do by which they can tell one effect from the other, the acceleration up or the gravitational pull down.

Einstein said simply that the two effects are equivalent, and that differences in a body's reaction to acceleration, called inertia, and its reaction to gravity, called gravitation, are artificial. He announced his principal of equivalence in 1911 and immediately applied it to a variety of problems. He already knew how to calculate the effect of acceleration on various phenomena, even when gravitation

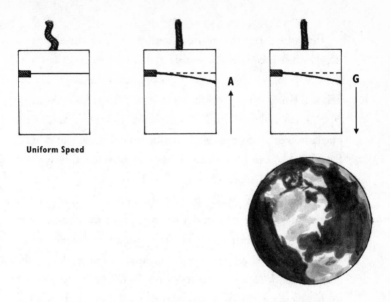

Uniform Speed

Figure 7.2. The principle of equivalence II: A light beam bends in the gravitational field G of the planet which is equivalent to acceleration A.

would not have been expected to produce any effect. Now he could replace gravitation by acceleration and look for the effects.

The first problem to which he applied his new principle was determining the path of a beam of light. To examine this we need to return to the lift in outer space. If a laser beam is fired from one side of the lift to the other when the lift is in uniform motion, the path of the laser beam will be a straight line. This is because the laser is moving at the same speed as the lift. To an observer inside the lift, it will hit the opposite side at the height from which it was fired.

However, a laser beam fired from one side to the other in a lift which is accelerating upwards will appear to an observer in the lift to follow a curved path, and to strike the opposite side below the height from which the laser was fired. Since the principle of equivalence states that the effects of acceleration and gravitation are the same, a gravitational field must also cause a light beam to bend. This was new and unexpected. Einstein had found a new equivalence for accelerated motion.

Einstein, who is usually thought of as a completely theoretical creature of mathematics and geometry, suggested shortly after announcing the principle of equivalence that an experiment carried out during a total eclipse of the Sun would test the idea of the gravitational deflection of light. 'As the fixed stars in the parts of the sky near the Sun are visible during total eclipses of the Sun, the consequence of the theory may be compared with experiment,' he stated.

The principle of equivalence was a key part but nevertheless a small part of the elaborate theory of general relativity. With help from Marcel Grossman, who was expert in just the branch of mathematics which he needed, Einstein formulated a final set of equations which fulfilled his aesthetic criterion that the laws of physics will be the same for uniform or accelerated motion. He found that the concept of a force of gravity was no longer necessary. Newton's gravitation was replaced by Einstein's curved space.

Now confident that he had the correct equations, Einstein immediately applied them to the unusual orbital motion of the planet closest to the Sun, Mercury. Newton's theory had been unable to explain the marked drift of the perihelion point of Mercury's orbit around the Sun. All the planets perturb one another through their gravitational pulls. One effect of this is that their elliptical orbits are themselves rotating, so that a planet's perihelion – the point at which it is closest to the Sun – moves a little further around the Sun at each orbit. In Mercury's case, this advance of the perihelion was greater than could be explained by Newtonian gravitation. Einstein's new theory predicted exactly the difference between the observed drift and the drift predicted from Newtonian theory. He showed that where gravity is weaker, for example at points in the Solar System farther from the Sun than Mercury's orbit, the new theory reduced to the Newtonian formulation. This must be true, since Newton's theory had been successfully confirmed by all calculations based on gravitation for over three hundred years, except in the case of the advance of Mercury's perihelion.

Finally, Einstein calculated the angle through which a light beam would bend if it just grazed the edge of the Sun. The general relativity theory predicted a displacement of 1.75 seconds of arc. This was exactly twice the value calculated using Newton's mechanics applied to light considered as a stream of particles. This may seem a very small angle (there are 3,600 seconds of arc in one degree), but it could be measured quite accurately with a good telescope. Einstein knew this and suggested that a precise photographic study of the eclipsed Sun could decide between his own theory of gravitation and that of Isaac Newton.

EXPERIMENTAL CONFIRMATION

Einstein announced the final results in a fifty-page paper published in the *Annalen der Physik* in 1916, describing his new theory, which he called general relativity. As soon as the theory was announced, a colleague of Einstein's, Erwin Freundlich of the Potsdam Observatory near Berlin, examined photographs of past eclipses, but they were inconclusive. Astronomers at the Lick Observatory in the USA tried to photograph the solar eclipse of 8 June 1918 but were defeated by cloudy skies. When the First World War ended with the armistice of November 1918, the idea was taken up by the British.

Einstein's plan was simple and practical. First, the date of the next total solar eclipse to occur after the war had to be looked up. Then a large telescope and high-resolution camera had to be transported to a location on the path of totality and set up to photograph the eclipsed Sun. At the moment of second contact, when the Moon completely covers the Sun for the first time, stars would appear around the Sun in the darkened sky. Light from these stars, having travelled vast distances for tens, hundreds or even thousands of years, would pass near the outer rim of the eclipsed Sun, enter the camera and record images on the photographic plate. If Einstein was right, these beams would be bent by the curvature of space near the Sun caused by the Sun's strong gravitational field, and would be deviated along a new path before reaching the camera on Earth. To detect the shift in the apparent

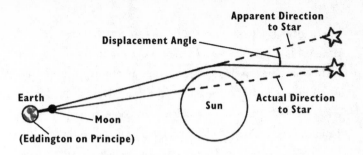

Figure 7.3. Measurement of the bending of starlight during a solar eclipse. The observer on Earth (Eddington) sees the star at the edge of the eclipsed Sun. The star is actually behind the Sun.

position of the stars, it would be necessary to compare the photographs of the displaced positions with photographs of the same field of stars taken when the Sun was in a different position and the starlight would not be deviated.

It goes without saying that for this experiment to succeed, the sky had to be clear, the resolution of the camera had to be high enough to produce sharply focused star images on the photographic plates, and there had to be sufficiently bright stars visible in the vicinity of the eclipsed Sun. Clearly, there is not much that experimenters could do about the vagaries of the weather. But they could make certain that the camera was up to the task, and they could also select an eclipse that took place against a bright star field. This last requirement could be a problem because there are only on average two eclipses each year.

Given the rarity of a total solar eclipse and the scarcity of bright stars along the Sun's annual path, astronomers might expect to wait years for a suitable opportunity. But this was not to be so. If astronomers had a free choice of the optimum star field behind the Sun for such an eclipse photo-experiment, they would probably choose the day of the year when the Sun, in its journey through the constellations of the zodiac, is positioned in the middle of the bright star cluster in Taurus called the Hyades. The Sun is in the Hyades on 29 May each year. Imagine the enthusiasm when it was realised that the next total solar eclipse, the first since the end of the war, would fall on 29 May 1919. Furthermore, this particular eclipse was to be 6 minutes and 50 seconds in duration, close to the theoretical maximum.

It is not surprising that while the war was still in progress, Sir Frank Dyson (1868–1939), the Astronomer Royal, had seized the opportunity for testing Einstein's theory which this particularly favourable eclipse would afford. He obtained a Government grant of £1,000 and naturally turned to Eddington, a long-standing member of the Royal Observatory staff, for help with planning the expedition.

Eddington, as Secretary of the Royal Astronomical Society during the war years, had maintained a constant communication with cosmologist Willem de Sitter in neutral Holland. De Sitter had sent Eddington copies of all Einstein's papers on the developing theory, even before they were published. Eddington had become translator and popular expositor of the difficult general relativity theory for English readers. He seemed destined to play an important role in the drama of the eclipse test.

It has generally been understood that, as the leading proponent of Einstein's new theory and one of the world's top astronomers, Eddington was the driving force behind the eclipse expedition. But this is not true. For one thing, he had no doubt that Einstein's theory was correct, and did not feel that it was necessary to confirm the predictions with such a difficult experiment as photographing a solar eclipse. But he was drawn into the project by Dyson, and a rather fortuitous set of circumstances resulting from his pacifist beliefs.

For a properly planned eclipse expedition, preparations would have to begin about two years beforehand. Although Dyson did have his small grant, it was impossible to ask any instrument-maker for help when the war effort had first call on resources. And there were other complications as well. Eddington, an able-bodied thirty-four-year-old male, was subject to the call-up. But as a devout Quaker, it was well known that he would claim deferment as a conscientious objector and end up peeling potatoes in a camp in northern England with other pacifists.

The Cambridge big shots argued effectively with the authorities that it was not in the country's best interests to have such a distinguished scientist as Eddington serve in the army. They no doubt used the sad case of the brilliant young crystallographer Henry Mosely, killed at Gallipoli, to convince them. Finally, Eddington received a letter of deferment from the Home Office. All he had to do was sign and return it. But the bloody-minded Eddington insisted on adding a postscript saying that if he was not deferred in the present instance, he would claim it anyway as a conscientious objector.

Much to the frustration of the Cambridge crowd, the Home Office reacted angrily to Eddington's response, and prepared to pack him off with the other pacifists. But Dyson, as Astronomer Royal, intervened directly. In the end, Eddington was deferred with a stipulation that if the war should end before May 1919, he should undertake to lead an eclipse expedition to verify Einstein's theory. Clearly, Dyson's influence had been felt!

A joint committee of the Royal Society and the Royal Astronomical Society, headed by the Astronomer Royal, was set up to organise the project. They planned two separate expeditions: one to Sobral, Brazil and the other to the island of Principe off the coast of West Africa. As the war ended, Eddington admitted to Dyson that he had an intense spiritual feeling about the expedition. He chose to go to Principe and was given permission to take with him the high-quality lens of the Oxford astrographic telescope. He sailed in early March for Lisbon.

PRINCIPE: ECLIPSE OF 29 MAY 1919

Eddington arrived on Principe in good time. For weeks he fussed with the telescope's mounting, which apparently was acting erratically. He knew that the images of the displaced stars would have to be photographed very carefully during the eclipse. A high degree of accuracy would be necessary to differentiate between Einstein's prediction of the displacement of starlight at the edge of the Sun of 1.75 seconds of arc and that based on Newton's theory of half that value, 0.875 seconds of arc. He built a special observing hut and eliminated all possible sources of vibration in the support of the telescope. Finally, there was nothing to do but wait for the new Moon's path to cross the Sun's on the ecliptic.

From 10 May onwards rain fell every day. On the fateful 29th, as the moment for the eclipse approached, the Sun was completely obscured by clouds. The despairing Eddington, praying for a miracle, pointed his telescope at the Sun and removed the shield covering the photographic plate. As the eclipse began he removed the lens cap from the telescope and took several photographs of a dark cloudy sky. As the 400 seconds of totality ticked by, Eddington could see no stars in the view. Then, suddenly, the miracle. The clouds began to evaporate and a few stars became visible for just a moment. He quickly exposed a fresh plate before the Sun appeared again from behind the Moon's shadow.

From his own notebook, Eddington's personal account of the expedition reveals his frustration on the day of the eclipse:

> We got our first sight of Principe in the morning of April 23 and soon found we were in clover, everyone anxious to give every help we needed. About May 16 we had no difficulty in getting the check photographs on three different nights. I had a good deal of work

measuring these. On May 29 a tremendous rainstorm came on. The rain stopped about noon and about 1.30, when the partial phase was well advanced, we began to get a glimpse of the Sun. We had to carry out our programme of photographs in faith. I did not see the eclipse, being too busy changing plates, except for one glance to make sure it had begun and another half-way through to see how much cloud there was. We took 16 photographs. They are all good of the Sun, showing a very remarkable prominence; but the cloud has interfered with the star images. The last six photographs show a few images which I hope will give us what we need.

He developed the plates and found star images on only one of them. Eagerly, he made tentative micrometer measurements of the displacement of several stars. To his delight he found an average displacement angle of 1.61 seconds of arc. This value favoured Einstein's new theory over Newton's. As Eddington put it a few days later in his journal:

June 3. I developed the photographs, 2 each night for 6 nights after the eclipse, and I spent the whole day measuring. The cloudy weather upset my plans and I had to treat the measures in a different way from what I intended, consequently I have not been able to make any preliminary announcement of the result. But the one plate that I measured gave a result agreeing with Einstein.

Eddington never forgot that day, and on one occasion in later years he referred to it as the 'greatest moment of his life'. Upon returning to England, the eclipse photographs were analysed very carefully before the results were communicated. By September rumours had reached Einstein that the eclipse results were favourable. Even though the war was now over, Eddington was still communicating via his colleague de Sitter in Holland. On 22 September Einstein received a telegram from his friend, the respected Dutch physicist Hendrik Lorentz, that Eddington had found the full deflection of the starlight in agreement with general relativity. The nearly unbelieving son immediately sent a postcard to his ailing mother in Switzerland: 'Dear Mother, Good news today. H. A. Lorentz has wired me that the British expedition has actually proved the light deflection near the Sun.' It would appear from this message that Einstein was slightly uncertain how the eclipse result would turn out. This may have been true. But he was never uncertain about the theory itself, as is clear by an incident from this period which would be recounted in the common rooms of physics and astronomy departments the world over.

A student of Einstein's at the University of Berlin in 1919, Ilse Rosenthal-Schneider, told how one day when she was studying with him, he suddenly interrupted the discussion and reached for a telegram that was on the window sill. He handed it to her with the words, 'Here, this will perhaps interest you.' It was the cable from Eddington with the results of the eclipse

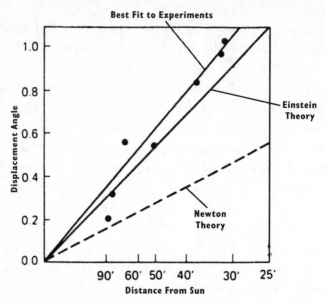

Figure 7.4. The results of the British eclipse expedition, 29 May 1919. Note that the line drawn through experimental measurements is much closer to Einstein's theory than to Newton's. (Philosophical Transactions of the Royal Society, Vol. 220, 1919)

measurements. After she expressed her joy that the results coincided with his calculations, he said, quite unmoved, 'But I knew that the theory is correct.' She then asked Einstein how he would have felt if there had been no confirmation of his prediction. He replied, 'Then I would have been sorry for the dear Lord, because the theory is correct.'

Einstein replied shortly afterwards to his English colleague, addressing him 'Lieber Herr Eddington!' The first paragraph of the letter reads (in translation):

Above all I should like to congratulate you on the success of your difficult expedition. Considering the great interest you have taken in the theory of relativity even in earlier days I think I can assume that we are indebted primarily to your initiative for the fact that these expeditions could take place. I am amazed at the interest which my English colleagues have taken in the theory in spite of its difficulty.

But the news was still unofficial. On 6 November 1919, a historic joint meeting of the Royal Society and the Royal Astronomical Society was held in London. In 1703, more than two centuries earlier, Newton had been elected President of the Royal Society, and annually thereafter he had been re-elected till his death. Now, in 1919, he was vividly present in the minds of the assembled scientists. His portrait, in its place of honour on the wall, dominated the scene. Yet though he faced the audience, it seemed as though his eyes were turned sharply to the right as the Astronomer Royal officially announced that 'the results of the expedition can leave little doubt that a deflection of light takes place in the neighbourhood of the Sun and that it is of the amount demanded by Einstein's general theory of relativity'.

At the conclusion of the meeting, J. J. Thomson, discoverer of the electron, Nobel laureate and President of the Royal Society, publicly hailed Einstein's work as 'one of the greatest – perhaps the greatest – of achievements in the history of human

Figure 7.5. Einstein, the maker of a new universe, arrives in New York City in 1922.

thought'. The drama of the occasion was undoubtedly heightened by the war that had just ended. A new theory of the universe, the brain-child of a German Jew working in Berlin, had been confirmed by an English Quaker on a small African island.

The poignancy of these events was heightened a few days later by the Armistice celebrations in the streets of London, which recalled the euphoria that had greeted the end of the war a year before. The validation of Einstein's theory by the confirmation of the predicted deflection of starlight had taken place under circumstances of high drama. At a time when nations were war-weary and heartsick, the bent rays of starlight had brightened a world in shadow, revealing a unity of humankind that transcended war. The deflected starlight had dazzled the public. But fate had played an unexpected trick — suddenly Einstein was world-famous. This essentially simple man, a cloistered seeker of cosmic beauty, was now an international icon, the focus of universal adoration.

Einstein's elevation to something approaching sainthood started with headlines in the London *Times*. An article headed 'The Fabric of the Universe' explaining the Eddington expedition and its purpose, concluded that 'It is confidently believed by the greatest experts that enough has been done to overthrow the certainty of ages and to require a new philosophy, one that will sweep away nearly all that has been hitherto accepted as the axiomatic basis of physical thought.'

The Times was not the only major newspaper to trumpet the general theory and Eddington's eclipse expedition. The *New York*

Times of Sunday, 9 November 1919, carried a three-column article under the headline 'Eclipse Showed Gravity Variation: Hailed as Epoch-Making'. After describing the expedition, the article stated, 'The evidence in favor of the gravitational bending of light was overwhelming, and there was a decidedly stronger case for the Einstein shift than for the Newtonian one.' It went on to quote J. J. Thomson's assessment of the experimental verification: 'It is not a discovery of an outlying island, but of a whole continent of new scientific ideas of the greatest importance to some of the most fundamental questions connected with physics.'

Perhaps Eddington himself should be allowed the last word. An anecdote, which for many years was thought to be apocryphal, was confirmed by the physicist and Nobel laureate Subrahmanyan Chandrasekhar in a memorial lecture on Eddington several years ago. The story was told to Chandrasekhar by Eddington himself. The story goes that as the November 1919 joint meeting of the Royal Society and the Royal Astronomical Society was breaking up, a reporter came up to Eddington and asked, 'Professor Eddington, I hear that you are one of only three persons in the world who understand general relativity.' Eddington, somewhat bemused, scratched his head. 'Don't be modest, Eddington,' the reporter said. The unassuming professor replied, 'Oh no, on the contrary, I am trying to think who the third person is.'

At the end of the second millennium it is now accepted that from this masterwork of Einstein's have sprung all our modern ideas about cosmology. This includes the Big Bang theory, the expanding

Figure 7.6. Eddington and Einstein meet for the first time, in Leiden in 1923 (clockwise: Einstein, Paul Ehrenfest, Willem de Sitter, Hendrik Lorentz and Eddington).

universe and stellar evolution. Discoveries of pulsars, quasars and black holes have eliminated all theories of gravitation save one, general relativity. Only now, as modern astrophysics probes deeper and deeper into space, are we coming to accept that we do indeed inhabit a curved universe, the one described by Einstein.

As solar eclipses continue through the twenty-first century and beyond, this story will be retold again and again. Certainly British scientists should never forget the pacifist Cambridge professor who, instead of peeling potatoes in May 1919, photographed the 32nd solar eclipse in saros cycle 136 from the island of Principe, and changed the world of physics and astronomy for ever.

THE LAST ECLIPSE
OF THE
MILLENNIUM

11 August 1999

Oh, dark, dark, dark amid the blaze of noon,
Irrecoverably dark, total eclipse
Without all hope of day

Milton, *Samson Agonistes*

'O, swear not by the Moon, th'inconstant Moon,
That monthly changes in her circled orb …'

William Shakespeare, *Romeo and Juliet*

W EDNESDAY, 11 AUGUST 1999 will see the last total solar eclipse of the twentieth century. The path of totality, where the Moon's umbral shadow tracks across the Earth's surface, starts in the Atlantic Ocean and crosses central Europe and the Middle East, ending at sunset in the Bay of Bengal. A partial eclipse will be seen within the much broader path of the Moon's penumbral shadow, which includes north-eastern North America, all of Europe, northern Africa and the western half of Asia. The totally eclipsed Sun will be visible across Europe, as most of the path passes across densely popu-lated areas. It could be the most widely viewed eclipse in history.

A global view of the eclipse path is shown in Figure 8.1. On this map, vertically drawn lines denoting the position of the umbra at different times are labelled in UT, Universal Time. This is a time-scale used by astronomers which is independent of time zones. To convert to British Summer Time (BST), add one hour to UT. Looking closely at the grid lines on the map, it can be seen that the Moon's shadow sweeps over the British Isles between 10:00 and 10:30 UT, or 11:00 and 11:30 BST.

Like every other eclipse, the 11 August 1999 event is part of a saros series: it is the twenty-first eclipse of saros series 145. All eclipses in this series occur at the Moon's ascending node, and sub-

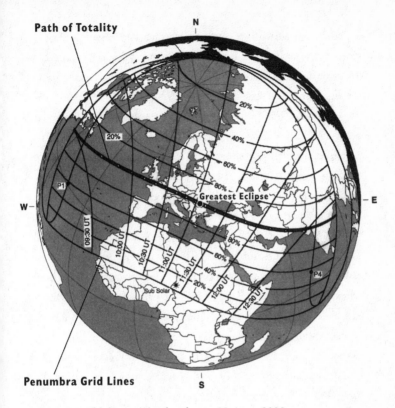

Path of Totality

N

20%

20%

40%

60%

80%

P1

Greatest Eclipse

W —

— E

09:30 UT

10:00 UT

10:30 UT

11:00 UT

80%

80%

11:30 UT

40%

12:00 UT

20%

Sub Solar

12:30 UT

P4

Penumbra Grid Lines

S

Figure 8.1. Global view of the solar eclipse on 11 August 1999.

sequent eclipses in the series progress southward, in the opposite direction from the eclipses of saros series 136, described in Chapter 3, which take place at a descending node. This is a convenient rule of thumb: even-numbered saros series occur at a descending node, odd-numbered series occur at an ascending node.

Saros series 145 is a young one, which began with a minuscule partial eclipse at high northern latitudes on 4 January 1639. After fourteen partial eclipses of increasing magnitude, the first annular eclipse occurred on 6 June 1891. The event was of 6-seconds duration, and the path swept through eastern Siberia and the Arctic Ocean. Although on this occasion the tip of the umbra fell just short of the Earth's surface, the Moon's distance from the Earth at each subsequent eclipse in the series gradually decreased, and the umbra struck the Earth at the very next eclipse, on 17 June 1909.

The third central eclipse of Saros 145 occurred on 29 June 1927. It was the first total eclipse of the series, and the path passed across England in addition to Scandinavia and Siberia. In the next eclipse in the series, on 9 July 1945 the path of totality began in Idaho and quickly swept north-east through Montana, Saskatchewan and Manitoba. After crossing Hudson Bay, Greenland and the North Atlantic, the umbra returned to Scandinavia and Siberia. The fifth central eclipse occurred on 20 July 1963. Its path crossed Alaska, central and eastern Canada, and Maine. The last eclipse of the series before 11 August 1999 took place on 31 July 1981. Its path crossed central Siberia, Sakhalin Island and the Pacific Ocean, where it ended north of Hawaii.

One saros cycle later, on 11 August 1999, the last solar eclipse of the millennium arrives. The path of totality starts at sunrise about 300 km to the south of Nova Scotia, where the Moon's umbral shadow begins its journey at 10:30:57 BST. At this hour on mainland Britain, the Sun has already been above the horizon for a few hours. The first observers at sea to view the eclipse at sunrise will enjoy a mere 47 seconds of totality. At this point the width of the shadow is 49 km.

For the next 40 minutes, as the shadow sweeps across the North Atlantic, passing through several time zones, it does not touch any land. It reaches the Isles of Scilly off the south-western coast of England at 11:10 BST. Here the Sun is 45° above the eastern horizon. The eclipse duration is 2 minutes at the central line of the eclipse, and the path width has expanded to 103 km. The shadow now pursues its easterly track with a ground velocity of 54.6 km per minute.

Somewhere in this region of the shadow's journey, the supersonic jetliner Concorde is scheduled to fly into the umbra. As a publicity stunt for the world's fastest jet, Concorde will attempt to keep up with the umbra as it crosses the Atlantic, affording its occupants a prolonged view of the fully eclipsed Sun. But Concorde's best effort will not be enough to keep up with the moving shadow. The plane's cruising speed is approximately 45 km per minute. As a result, the shadow will outpace it by about 10 km per minute. Since the diameter of the shadow is 103 km, Concorde's passengers will experience totality for about 10 minutes.

At 11:11 BST the Moon's umbra will touch the British mainland for the first time since 1927 (it won't be back until the year 2090). The shadow will track across the mainland for just 4 minutes. Its much-anticipated arrival along the shores of the Cornish Peninsula will give eager observers a brief taste of totality. Plymouth, the largest English city in the path, is north of the centre-line and witnesses a total phase lasting 1 minute 39 seconds. However, 1 minute and 35 seconds before the umbra reaches Plymouth it passes over Falmouth, which is directly on the centre-line of the eclipse.

A sky-watcher's view at the seaside town of Falmouth on this special morning will never be forgotten. At 9:57:06 BST the Sun, 36° above the horizon, will just be touched by the Moon at first contact. Over the next period of 1 hour, 14 minutes and 9 seconds more and more of the Sun's disk will be covered by the Moon, and the sky will gradually darken. Birds will stop chirping, flowers will close up and the impression of sunset will be created. Street lights activated by light levels will switch on.

The safest and most inexpensive method of observing the eclipse is by projection. A pinhole or small opening in a suitably large sheet of material will form an image of the Sun on a screen placed about a metre behind it. Alternatively, the many gaps in a loosely woven straw hat, or even the spaces between interlaced fingers, can be used to cast a pattern of solar images onto a screen. A similar effect is seen on the ground below a broadleaf tree: the many 'pinholes' formed by overlapping leaves create hundreds of crescent-shaped images of the eclipsed Sun.

Binoculars or a small telescope mounted on a tripod can also be used to project a magnified image of the Sun onto a white card positioned behind the eyepiece. All of these methods will provide a safe view of the partial phases of the eclipse. However, it is essential to ensure that no one looks at the Sun through any optical instrument. The main advantage of the projection methods is that nobody is looking directly at the Sun. The disadvantage of pinhole method is that the screen must be placed at least a metre behind the opening to get a solar image that is large enough to see easily.

Observing the Sun can be dangerous if you do not take the proper precautions. While environmental exposure to UV radiation is known to contribute to the accelerated ageing of the outer layers of the eye and the development of cataracts, the concern over improper viewing of the Sun during an eclipse is for the development of 'eclipse blindness' or retinal burns. The result is a loss of visual function which may be either temporary or permanent, depending on the severity of the damage.

The only time the Sun can be viewed safely with the naked eye is during the total phase of a total eclipse, when the Moon completely covers the disk of the Sun. It is never safe to look at a partial or annular eclipse, or the partial phases of a total solar eclipse, without the proper equipment and techniques. Even when 99 per cent of the Sun's surface, the photosphere, is obscured during the partial phases of a solar eclipse, the remaining crescent Sun is still intense enough to cause a retinal burn, even though illumination levels are comparable to twilight. Failure to use proper observing methods may result in permanent eye damage or severe visual loss.

At any time other than during totality, the Sun must be viewed through a filter specially designed to protect the eyes. Most filters have a thin layer of chromium alloy or aluminium deposited on their surfaces that attenuate both visible and near-infrared radiation. A safe solar filter should allow less than 0.003 per cent of the Sun's light to pass through it.

These warnings can never be repeated too often. *To look directly at the Sun is to risk permanent blindness. Looking at the Sun through binoculars or a telescope increases the risk enormously.*

The eclipse may be safely photographed provided the above precautions are followed. Any kind of camera with manual controls can be used to capture this spectacular event. However, a lens with a long focal length is recommended so as to produce as large an image of the Sun as possible. A standard 50 mm lens yields a minuscule 0.5 mm image, while a 200 mm telephoto or zoom lens produces a 1.9 mm image. A focal length of 500 mm will give a solar image of 4.6 mm. All these are shown in actual size on 35 mm film in Figure 8.2, together with images obtained with lenses of very long focal length.

As the sky darkens for viewers in Falmouth, the planets Mercury and Venus will become visible, even before totality arrives. The last beams of sunlight pass between mountains at the Moon's edge to form Baily's beads and the diamond ring effect. And then, at 11:11:15 BST, second contact occurs and totality begins. As the 2 minutes and 6 seconds of totality start, the solar corona, the most distinguishing feature of a total

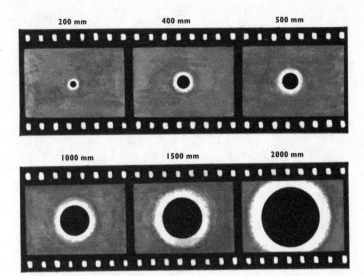

Figure 8.2. Field of View of the eclipsed Sun on 35 mm film (actual size) for the same refracting telescope at various focal lengths. To photograph the Sun's corona, the focal length should not exceed 1500 mm.

eclipse, springs into view. After 63 seconds totality is half over. This is the moment of maximum eclipse, with the Sun in a south-easterly direction, 50° east of due south and 46° above the horizon. The Sun is still climbing in the sky as it has not yet passed the local meridian, which occurs nominally at noon.

Figure 8.3 shows the view of the sky from Falmouth at the time of totality. Around the eclipsed Sun can be seen stars and planets hidden by the glare of the Sun only a few seconds before. The planets Jupiter and Saturn will be setting in the west and may be difficult to identify. However, as mentioned above,

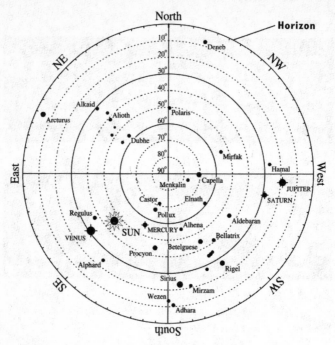

Figure 8.3. View of the sky around the eclipsed Sun at Falmouth on 11 August 1999. To locate celestial objects, hold the map overhead with 'South' pointing towards the Sun. The centre of the diagram is directly overhead; the outside rim is the horizon.

Mercury and Venus, the two inferior planets (those whose orbits are closer to the Sun than the Earth's) should be quite easy to find. Mercury is 18° west of the Sun and Venus 15° to its east, both quite bright in the darkening sky. Venus will be shining so brightly that it will be impossible to miss it during totality. Mercury will prove much more challenging, but not too difficult if the sky transparency is good. For many people this will be their first view of Mercury, as its orbit is very close to the Sun and it is normally difficult to observe. Under the right circumstances, it should be possible to view all five of these planets. At the time of the eclipse the Sun is in the constellation of Cancer, a region of the sky devoid of bright stars. However, bright stars which are relatively close to the eclipsed Sun include Sirius, Regulus, Castor, Pollux and Procyon.

The adventurous and experienced observer may wish to look for something that is rare at any time but would be an astonishing sight during an eclipse. When the Sun's rays have been totally obscured, it may be possible to see a meteor. The Perseid meteor shower, one of the most reliable and spectacular in the sky, reaches the peak of its activity between 10 and 12 August each year. Its radiant, the point in the sky from which the meteors appear to originate, is located about 50° above the western horizon, near the star Mirfak, which is shown in Figure 8.3. Meteors, or shooting stars as they are popularly called, are in reality tiny pieces of cosmic debris burning up as they plunge into the Earth's atmosphere at tens of kilometres per second. In the 2 minutes 6 seconds of totality, it might just be possible to see one of these fiery tracks if it is exceptionally bright. Of course, the Perseid meteors can be seen in the night sky after the Sun sets, but it is particularly bizarre to spot one during the daytime hours.

At 11:13:21 BST the total eclipse is all over at Falmouth. This is the time of third contact, when the Moon begins to move off the Sun's disk. The corona disappears, and eyes should

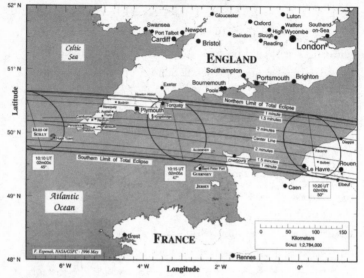

Figure 8.4. The path of totality between England and France. The umbra engulfs Alderney, one of the Channel Islands, before making contact with the French mainland.

be quickly protected against the harmful rays of direct sunlight streaming around the Moon's limb.

A few minutes after the corona disappears at Falmouth, at 11:16, the umbra leaves England and quickly traverses the English Channel, as shown in Figure 8.4. London misses the total phase but experiences partiality with a maximum magnitude of 0.968 (i.e. 96.8 per cent of the Sun's diameter will be obscured) at 11:20, when the eclipsed Sun crosses London's local meridian. At that instant, the umbra is just about touching the French coast near Dieppe, as shown on the map.

The Channel Islands of Guernsey and Jersey lie just south of the path, and witness a partial eclipse of magnitude 0.995. To the north, Alderney is deep in the path and enjoys over one and a half minutes of totality. A large group of astronomers from the United Kingdom attending a scientific meeting on Guernsey will cruise to the island of Alderney to observe the eclipse.

The umbra then crosses the English Channel, the Cherbourg peninsula, northern France, and the southern tip of Belgium and Luxembourg, and moves on to southern Germany. After passing over Austria, Hungary and the north-eastern tip of Yugoslavia, the eclipse reaches its maximum duration of totality over Romania before crossing the north-eastern part of Bulgaria and the Black Sea.

Not since 1961 has the Moon cast its dark shadow upon central Europe. The southern edge of the umbra first reaches the Normandy coast just as the northern edge leaves England. As the shadow speeds across the French countryside, its southern edge passes 30 km north of Paris, whose inhabitants will witness a partial event of magnitude 0.992 at 11:23 BST, or 12:23 p.m. local French time.

Continuing on its eastward track, the path's northern limit crosses into southern Belgium, Luxembourg and Germany. Stuttgart, lying near the path's centre, has 2 minutes 17 seconds of totality. Here the Sun stands at 55° above the horizon. The path is now 109 km wide, and the ground speed has dropped to 44.4 km per minute. Although Munich lies 20 km south of the

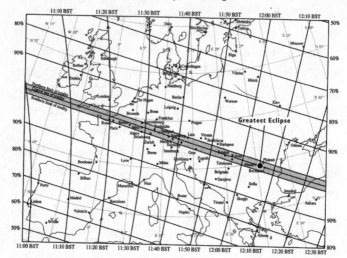

Total Solar Eclipse of 11 Aug 1999

Figure 8.5. The path of totality across Europe. The instant of greatest eclipse occurs at 12:03:04 BST near the Romanian capital of Bucharest.

centre-line, the city's two million citizens will still experience more than 2 minutes of totality.

The path across Europe can be followed in Figure 8.5, where the line of totality and the names of principal cities are indicated. At 11:41 BST the umbra leaves Germany and moves into Austria, where it crosses the eastern Alps. Vienna is almost 40 km north of the path and experiences a 0.990 magnitude partial eclipse. The southern edge of the path grazes north-eastern Slovenia as the shadow enters Hungary at 11:47 BST. Lake Balaton, a popular Hungarian resort, lies wholly within the path, and the umbra arrives there at 11:50 BST. Duration lasts

2 minutes 22 seconds. Like Vienna, Budapest is also about 40 km north of the path and enjoys a 0.991 magnitude partial eclipse. As the shadow leaves Hungary, it sweeps through northern Yugoslavia before continuing on into Romania.

The instant of greatest eclipse occurs at 12:03:04, when the axis of the Moon's shadow passes closest to the centre of the Earth. At that moment the shadow's centre is located among the rolling hills of south central Romania, very near Rîmnicu-Vîlcea as can be seen in Figure 8.6. Here the length of totality, the maximum for any point of the entire eclipse path, is 2 minutes and 23 seconds. This increase in duration is due to the increase in the 'slowing speed' of the shadow due to the Earth's rotation. The slowing speed is greatest when the Moon and the eclipsed Sun are at the local meridian. A few minutes later, Romania's capital city Bucharest is engulfed by the shadow. Continuing east—south-east, the path crosses the Romania/Bulgaria border before heading out across the Black Sea.

The next landfall occurs along the Black Sea coast of northern Turkey at 12:21 BST. For Ankara, 150 km south of the path, there is a 0.969 magnitude partial eclipse. The track diagonally bisects Turkey as it moves inland, while the duration centre-line begins a gradual but steady decrease. At 12:29 BST, Turhal falls deep within the shadow for 2 minutes 15 seconds. At just about this time, viewers in Falmouth will see the Moon finally move away from the Sun as the partial eclipse phase ends there, with fourth contact.

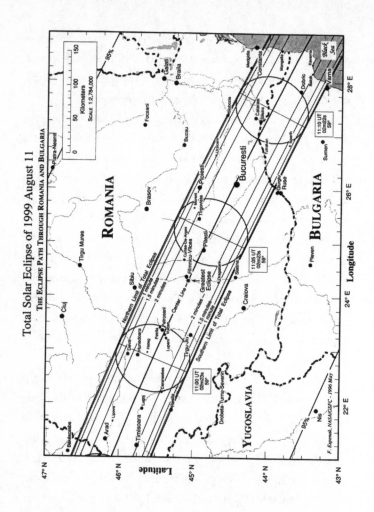

Figure 8.6. The path of the Moon's umbra in the vicinity of the position of greatest eclipse, near the Romanian capital of Bucharest.

The umbra now reaches Turkey's south-eastern border at 12:45 BST and briefly enters north-western Syria as it crosses into Iraq. The centre-line duration is now 2 minutes 5 seconds, with the Sun's altitude at 50°. At Baghdad, 220 km south of the path, there is a partial eclipse of magnitude 0.940. Arriving at Iran's western border, the shadow spends the next half-hour crossing sparsely populated mountain ranges and deserts. The inhabitants of Tehran, north of the path, will witness a 0.943 magnitude partial eclipse. At 13:22 BST the shadow enters Pakistan and skirts the shores of the Arabian Sea. Karachi is near the centre-line and experiences 1 minute 13 seconds of totality with the Sun 22° above the western horizon. By now the path width has shrunk to 85 km, while the shadow's speed has increased to 120 km per minute.

The umbra arrives in India, the last nation in its path, at 13:28 BST. As the shadow sweeps across the subcontinent, its velocity rapidly increases while the duration of the eclipse on the centre-line drops to less than a minute. At this point the Sun is only 7° above the horizon. The 11 million inhabitants of Calcutta will witness a 0.879 magnitude partial eclipse with the Sun a scant 2° above the western horizon. Leaving India just north of Vishakhapatnam, the shadow sweeps into the Bay of Bengal where it moves off the Earth and back into space at exactly 13:36:23 BST, not to return until the next millennium. Over the course of 3 hours and 7 minutes, the Moon's umbra will have travelled a path approximately 14,000 km long at an average speed of 4500 km/h, about twice the cruising speed of Concorde.

The next time an eclipse from saros series 145 returns to the Earth will be on 21 August 2017, 18 years and 10.32 days after 11 August 1999. It will be the first total solar eclipse visible from the continental United States since 1979. The path of totality in 2017 will stretch from Oregon through Idaho, Wyoming, Nebraska, Missouri, Illinois, Kentucky and Tennessee. The longest period of totality will be in the Carolinas, and has a duration of 2 minutes and 40 seconds.

From the twenty-first to the twenty-fourth century inclusive, Saros 145 will continue to produce total solar eclipses of increasing duration as the path of each event shifts southward. By the time the midpoint of the series is reached on 25 February 2324, the duration of totality will exceed 4 minutes. The duration continues to increase into the twenty-fifth and twenty-sixth centuries. The maximum duration of totality peaks at 7 minutes 12 seconds on 25 June 2522. In the remaining six umbral eclipses, the duration rapidly drops but is still almost 3 minutes at the final total eclipse of the series, on 9 September 2648.

Over the next three and a half centuries there will be twenty partial eclipses of progressively decreasing magnitude occuring. The final event, the 77th in the series, will take place on 17 April 3009 over the polar regions of the southern hemisphere. The saros series that produces the last eclipse of the second millennium will thus continue into the fourth millennium.

Figure 8.7. The last eclipse of the millennium.

GLOSSARY

Ångström One hundred millionth of a centimetre. Has the symbol Å.

Annular Eclipse A solar eclipse in which the moon does not completely cover the Sun. A ring of sunlight is seen around the black disk of the Moon.

Anomalistic Month Period of time for the Moon to travel from apogee to perigee and back again to apogee.

Aphelion Point in the Earth's orbit that is farthest from the Sun.

Apogee A point in the Moon's orbit that is farthest from the Earth.

Ascending Node A point in the orbit of the Moon, or any orbit, when it crosses the ecliptic from below to above the ecliptic plane (see also descending node).

Baily's beads The breaking up of sunlight, visible at the edge of the Moon's disk just before the appearance of a total eclipse. Caused by the streaming of sunlight between mountains at the edge of the Moon.

Celestial sphere An Earth-centred model of the heavens in which the motion of the stars, the planets, the Sun and the Moon are projected on to a large imaginary crystal dome.

Central Eclipse A total or annular eclipse.

Corona The hot outer atmosphere of the Sun which appears as a halo during a total eclipse.

Cuneiform The writing used on clay tablets in Mesopotamia during the second and third Millennia BC.

Descending Node The point in the orbit of the Moon when it crosses from above to below the ecliptic.

Diamond Ring Effect The last remaining bead of light of Baily's beads, which shines just before and just after the total phase of a solar eclipse. It has the appearance of a diamond ring.

Draconic Month The time it takes for the Moon to complete one cycle and return to the same node, the same point where the Moon's orbit crosses the ecliptic.

Eclipse Season The period when the Sun is close to alignment with a lunar node. This is the period when eclipses may take place, and occurs every 173 days.

Eclipse Year The interval between successive passes of the Sun past the same lunar node, approximately 346.62 days.

Ecliptic The path of the Sun around the sky as it appears from the Earth.

Elliptical Orbit The oval-shaped path of an orbital body circling another attracting body which has a precise mathematical formulation.

Ephemerides Tables of the position of the Sun and the Moon at different times.

Ephemeris A table giving the changing position of any celestial body in an orbit.

First Contact The beginning of a solar eclipse when the edge of the Moon first touches the complete disk of the Sun.

Fourth Contact The end of the solar eclipse when the disk of the Moon completely breaks away from the disk of the Sun.

Geocentric Describing an Earth-centred model of the solar system in which celestial bodies are thought to be revolving around the Earth.

Heliocentric Describing a model in which the Earth and other celestial bodies revolve about the Sun.

Latitude Angular distance on the Earth north or south of the equator.

Longitude Angular distance on the Earth either east or west of the prime meridian at Greenwich.

Lunar Eclipse The appearance of the shadow of the Earth falling across the full Moon.

Node Point in the sky at which the orbital path of the Moon crosses the ecliptic, the path of the Sun.

Partial Eclipse An eclipse in which the observer sees only part of the Sun obscured by the Moon.

Penumbra Part of the shadow within which the light source is only partially obscured. In the context of this book it means the outer part of the Moon's shadow.

Perigee The point in the orbit of the Moon that is closest to the Earth.

Perihelion The point in the orbit of the Earth that is closest to the Sun.

Prominence A massive gaseous formation above the surface of the Sun, which can be seen during a total eclipse.

Saros The eclipse cycle with a period of 223 synodic months or 6,585.32 days. After this time the Sun, Moon and Earth return to almost exactly the same relative positions.

Second Contact The beginning of the total phase of a solar eclipse. Starts when the leading edge of the Moon first completely obscures the Sun.

Solar Eclipse The passage of the new Moon between the Sun and the Earth in which the Moon's shadow is cast over the Earth.

Spectroscope An optical instrument that spreads light out into its individual wavelengths, which can then be measured.

Synodic Month The period of time from one full Moon to the next full Moon.

Third Contact The end of a total phase of a solar eclipse. The trailing edge of the Moon first uncovers the Sun.

Totality The period during the solar eclipse when the Sun is completely obscured by the Moon.

Umbra That part of a shadow in which the source of the light is completely hidden from the observer. In the context of this book it means the Moon's shadow.

Zodiac A band on the celestial sphere either side of the ecliptic divided into twelve equal parts of 30° each. Each part contains a specific constellation used to identify celestial objects moving along the ecliptic.

FURTHER READING

Bell, Steve, *The RGO Guide to the 1999 Total Eclipse of the Sun* (HM Nautical Almanac Office, Cambridge, 1997)

Black, J. A. and Green, A., *Gods, Demons and Symbols of Ancient Mesopotamia* (British Museum Press, London, 1992)

Brewer, Bryan, *Eclipse* (Earth View, Seattle, 1991)

Clark, Ronald W., *Einstein: The Life and Times* (Hodder & Stoughton, London, 1979).

Collon, D., *Ancient Near Eastern Art* (British Museum Press, London, 1995).

Comte, Auguste, *Cours de philosophie positive* (Paris, 1833)

Covington, M., *Astrophotography for the Amateur* (Cambridge University Press, Cambridge, 1988)

Einstein, A., 'Grundlage der allgemeinen Relativitätstheorie', *Annalen der Physik*, 1916, Vol. 49, pp. 769–822

Espenak, Fred, *Fifty Year Canon of Solar Eclipses*, NASA Reference Publication 1178 (Revised), (Sky Publishing, Cambridge, MA, 1994)

Espenak, F. and Anderson, J., *Total Solar Eclipse of 1999 August 11*, NASA Reference Publication 1398 (NASA, March 1997)

Fiala, A. D., DeYoung, J. A., and Lukac, M. R., *Solar Eclipses, 1991–2000*, USNO Circular No. 170 (US Naval Observatory, Washington, DC, 1986)

Gingerich, Owen, *The Great Copernicus Chase and Other Adventures in Astronomical History* (Sky Publishing, Cambridge, MA, 1992)

Golub, Leon and Pasachoff, Jay M., *The Solar Corona* (Cambridge University Press, Cambridge, 1997)

Hallo, W. W. and Simpson, W. K., *The Ancient Near East* (Harcourt Publishers, New York, 1971)

Hawkins, Gerald S., *Stonehenge Decoded* (Doubleday, New York, 1965)

Hoskin, Michael (ed.), *The Cambridge Illustrated History of Astronomy* (Cambridge University Press, Cambridge, 1997)

Hoyle, Fred, *From Stonehenge to Modern Astronomy* (Cambridge University Press, Cambridge, 1971)

Hoyle, Fred, *On Stonehenge* (W. H. Freeman & Co., San Francisco, 1977)

Kepler, Johannes, *The New Astronomy*, trans. William Donahue (Cambridge University Press, Cambridge, 1989)

Kudlek, Manfred and Mickler, Erich H., *Solar and Lunar Eclipses of the Ancient Near East* (Verlag Butzon & Bercker Kevelaer, Hamburg, 1971)

Littmann, M. and Willcox, K., *Totality, Eclipses of the Sun* (University of Hawaii Press, Honolulu, 1991)

Lowenthal, James, *The Hidden Sun: Solar Eclipses and Astrophotography* (Avon, New York, 1984)

Meeus, J., Grosjean, C. C. and Vanderleen, W., *Canon of Solar Eclipses* (Pergamon Press, Oxford, 1966)

Melville, Pauline, *The Ventriloquist's Tale* (Bloomsbury, London, 1997)

Menzel, Donald H. and Pasachoff, Jay M., *A Field Guide to the Stars and Planets* (2nd ed.), (Houghton Mifflin, Boston, 1990)

Neugebauer, Otto, *The Exact Sciences in Antiquity* (Princeton University Press, Princeton, 1952)

Neugebauer, Otto, *History of Ancient Mathematical Astronomy* (Springer Publishing Co., New York, 1975)

Newton, Isaac, *Philosophiae Naturalis Principia Mathematica*, Florian Cajori (ed.), (University of California Press, Berkeley, 1924), (first published in 1687)

North, John, *Stonehenge: Neolithic Man and the Cosmos* (HarperCollins, London, 1996)

Oates, Joan, *Babylon* (Thames & Hudson, London, 1986)

Oppolzer, Theodor R. von, *Canon of Eclipses* (Dover Publications, New York, 1962)

Panchenko, Dmitri, 'Thale's Prediction of a Solar Eclipse', *Journal of the History of Astronomy*, 1994, Vol. 25

Pasachoff, J. M. and Covington, M., *The Cambridge Eclipse Photography Guide* (Cambridge University Press, Cambridge, 1993)

Pasachoff, J. M. and Menzel, D. H., *Field Guide to the Stars and Planets* (3rd ed.), (Houghton Mifflin, Boston, 1992)

Saggs, H. W. F., *The Babylonians: Peoples of the Past* (British Museum Press, London, 1995)

Stephenson, F. R., *Historical Eclipses and Earth's Rotation* (Cambridge University Press, Cambridge, 1997)

Walker, C. B. F., *Cuneiform: Reading the Past* (British Museum Press, London, 1987)

Zirker, J. B., *Total Eclipses of the Sun* (Princeton University Press, Princeton, 1995)

ACKNOWLEDGEMENTS

It gives me great pleasure to thank the team who helped me put this book together. The timetable was tight and the hope was to have the book on the shelves before the August 1999 eclipse. So it couldn't be late.

First of all, a deep-felt appreciation to my determined and eclectic editor Leo Hollis. We were in daily contact during the last few weeks of the writing. He was indefatigable in correcting, changing, improving and, most important, clarifying the text. Christopher Potter was the inspiration behind the project and provided the final editing.

It is rare that a writer can have such an informed and patient copy-editor as John Woodruff. He and designer Robert Updegraff were unflappable at the critical stages, accepting changes up to the eleventh hour. Kathy Black played a crucial part for me, keying much of the material into the computer. She knows what deadlines are about.

The final member of the team was Mark McEvoy. His ability to handle images with a camera, with pen and ink or with a computer meant I could write in my most comfortable style, using many visuals. Without his partnership this book would look completely different. Finally, my wife Pat was a one-person support squad, keeping me encouraged, nourished and on track for the twelve weeks of this project.

It is rare that any book is published today on the history of astronomy without some recognition being given to Owen Gingerich of the Harvard-Smithsonian Center. This book is no exception. In particular, I wish to thank him for discussions on Stonehenge and allowing me to quote freely from his article on eighteenth-century eclipse paths. The publications of NASA – in particular, those of Fred Espenak and Jay Anderson – were very helpful. Bryan Brewer's information on the history of saros cycle 136 was also very important for my treatment.

Steve Bell of the Royal Greenwich Observatory helped me with useful conversations about the 1999 eclipse and provided some maps of the eclipse path. F. R. Stephenson of Durham University has also been most generous with his work related to ancient eclipses. Spencer Weart, Simon Schaffer and J. V. Field responded generously to my calls for help in their special areas of expertise.

I owe Michael Haggiag a debt for my interest in solar eclipses. It was under his auspices that I went to Baja in 1991 as part of our TV series on great discoveries in science. Some day we will finish that project.

INDEX

PICTURE CREDITS

All illustrations and artwork, other than those listed below, by Mark McEvoy.
Photographs from Baja California by Mark McEvoy.

Figures 1.2, 5.1, 6.5 Hulton Getty, London; Figure 1.8 after Phillip S. Harrington; Figure 2.3 British Museum, London; Figure 2.5 Stephenson, F. R., *Historical Eclipses and Earth's Rotation* (Cambridge University Press, Cambridge, 1997); Figure 4.2 Hawkins, Gerald S., *Stonehenge Decoded* (Doubleday, New York, 1965); Figure 5.2 Gingerich, Owen, *The Great Copernicus Chase and Other Adventures in Astronomical History* (Sky Publishing, Cambridge, MA, 1992); Figure 5.6 Fiala, A. D., DeYoung, J. A., and Lukac, M. R., *Solar Eclipses, 1991–2000*, USNO Circular No. 170 (US Naval Observatory, Washington, DC, 1986); Figure 6.8 *Illustrated London News*, 1871; Figure 7.5 Brown Brothers Agency, PA; Figure 7.6 Akademisch Historisch Museum, Leiden; Figures 8.1, 8.5, 8.6 Espenak, F. and Anderson, J., *Total Solar Eclipse of 1999 August 11*, NASA Reference Publication 1398 (NASA, March 1997); Figures 8.3 and 8.4 Royal Greenwich Observatory, London.